ENGLISH GRAMMAR RECITATION

Workbook Three

Student Book

Cheryl Lowe & Joyce Cothran

www.MemoriaPress.com

ENGLISH GRAMMAR RECITATION
Workbook Three

STUDENT BOOK
Cheryl Lowe & Joyce Cothran

ISBN 978-1-61538-391-7

First Edition

CONTENTS

UNIT I 11

Lesson 1: Capitalization Review 12
Lesson 2: Punctuation Review 14
Lesson 3: Punctuation Review 16
Lesson 4: Grammar Review 18
Lesson 5: Grammar Review 20
Unit I Review 24

UNIT II 27

Lesson 6: Sentence Complements 28
Lesson 7: Predicate Nominatives & Adjectives .. 30
Lesson 8: Linking Verbs 32
Lesson 9: Linking Verbs 34
Lesson 10: Direct Objects 36
Lesson 11: Complementary Infinitive 38
Lesson 12: Indirect Objects 40
Unit II Review: Sentence Complements 42

UNIT III 45

Lesson 13: Finding the Subject 46
Lesson 14: Finding the Subject 48
Lesson 15: Pronouns 50
Lesson 16: Possessive Pronouns 52
Lesson 17: Transitive and Intransitive Verbs .. 54
Lesson 18: Active and Passive Voice 56
Lesson 19: Active and Passive Voice 58
Unit III Review 60

UNIT IV 63

Lesson 20: Commas 64
Lesson 21: Quotation Marks 66
Lesson 22: Quotation Marks 68
Lesson 23: Adverbs 70
Lesson 24: Adverbs 72
Lesson 25: Conjunctions 74
Lesson 26: Conjunctions 76
Unit IV Review 78

Recitation 81
Capitalization & Punctuation Style Sheets 93
Diagramming 99

INTRODUCTION

The rationale for this program is that mastery of terms, definitions, and facts should precede mastery of application. A student who can't define the parts of speech, the parts of a sentence, phrase, clause, etc., doesn't have the tools he needs to understand and apply grammar successfully. Understanding comes over time as the student practices using the facts he has learned. This approach is consistent with the trivium and tradition as explained below.

The name grammar school comes from the early Renaissance, when the major subject of the elementary years was the Latin grammar. The young grammar student memorized Latin grammar forms—declensions and conjugations—and gradually transitioned to the more abstract study of Latin syntax and translation in his upper grammar school years. This plan of work was consistent with the trivium stages of learning—memorization for the younger grammar student and logic-level translation skills for the older.

As the study of Latin declined over the centuries, the study of English gradually took its place. English grammar, however, being irregular and lacking inflection, is in some ways more abstract and difficult for the young child than Latin. Although the technique of diagramming was developed to make the invisible English grammar more concrete, the study of English grammar in the grammar school years has remained a frustrating and often fruitless experience for both teachers and students. Experience has taught us that the logic-level skills of English grammar analysis and diagramming are difficult for the grammar school student and perhaps not the best use of academic time.

First let's clarify what we mean by the term "grammar." Most English grammar books are actually comprehensive language arts texts in which the grammar section is relatively small and the bulk of the text is devoted to punctuation, capitalization, composition, and English usage, all of which are important and appropriate for the grammar school student. But limiting ourselves to the question of analytical grammar, what should we be teaching our students in the elementary years?

I propose that we adopt the same plan as the Renaissance grammar schools, a plan that is consistent with the trivium and has been proven successful: memorization for the younger students and analysis/diagramming for the older ones. Students can memorize the terms and definitions of English grammar at a young age, although applying them successfully is quite difficult. I believe this memorization step is the missing component in our English grammar curriculum. Once students have a working knowledge of grammar terms and definitions, they are much better prepared to work with English grammar in the logic stage. This is the same plan used in the *First Form Latin* series—memorization of declensions and conjugations with limited application for the younger student, gradually transitioning to a study of syntax and translation for the older student in the logic stage.

For this plan, we need a grammar catechism for memorization and recitation, thus this *English Grammar Recitation,* a catechism of approximately 154 grammar questions/answers/examples organized systematically and divided into five sections of increasing difficulty, to be covered in five or more years, beginning as young as 3rd grade. The *English Grammar Recitation* is a manual of English grammar for the grammar stage—a convenient tool for memorization, reference, and review.

Each of the five sections of the catechism has a companion workbook covering approximately 30 questions, each with accompanying exercises. The purpose of the workbook exercises is to illustrate the grammar topic so the student has a preliminary understanding of what he is being asked to memorize. Application is practiced, but neither tested nor mastered. Analysis, diagramming, and understanding will always lag behind the memorization of the catechism. The goal is for the student, over the period of five years or more, to master this catechism as a foundation for a deeper and more thorough understanding in the logic stage.

A change in emphasis in these grammar years will give us a pedagogical approach that is more consistent with the trivium stages of learning. The trivium plan, after all, is to use the early years for memorization of the facts that will be used later for analysis, application, and mastery. Admittedly, memorization of a catechism is not easy, and the level of its mastery will vary among any group of students. That being said, implanting terms, definitions, and examples firmly in the minds of students will prepare them well for truly advanced study in the logic years.

We realize that memorization of this many rules is a real challenge, so we have marked with an asterisk (*) those rules that we feel are necessary for memorization by students. These are the rules that define grammar terms (ex. What is a noun?) and that give lists of words that are necessary for students to know (ex. Give all forms of the *to be* verb.). Students should be familiar with the rest of the rules, but memorization is not required.

A second objective of our *English Grammar Recitation* is to teach grammar topics in a sequence that more closely follows the Latin grammar, which in a classical education should serve as the primary language lesson. Each of the five workbooks, then, corresponds loosely to five levels of Memoria Press Latin, *Latina Christiana* through *Fourth Form Latin*. Regardless of the Latin program used, however, *English Grammar Recitation* should be an effective companion to your Latin study. It is hoped that this plan will increase understanding of both Latin and English as they reinforce each other.

English Grammar Recitation also covers capitalization and punctuation in the Style Sheets in the back of this manual. Practice of these rules is also included in the workbooks, as well as assessments focusing on the correct writing of examples from dictation.

TEACHING GUIDELINES

There are two components to *English Grammar Recitation*: grammar and capitalization/punctuation. The grammar recitation and the capitalization/punctuation style sheets are in the Appendix. Teaching guidelines for each component are explained below.

A. **Grammar.** The first unit is devoted to capitalization, so the grammar recitation doesn't begin until Unit II. Each lesson in Units II-IV contains two to four new grammar questions.

1. **Teach.** Write the grammar question and answer with examples, if any, on the board (an overhead or teaching from the text is fine), and explain, paying particular attention to spelling, pronunciation, and definitions of unfamiliar grammar terms. **Use the examples, if present, to explain the grammar concept.** Work toward understanding the questions, answers, and examples. When you feel students have a preliminary grasp of the lesson, recite questions and answers aloud with students several times. Students will need to look at their text while reciting at the beginning, but they should work toward mastery throughout the week in preparation for the weekly quiz. The rules marked with an asterisk (*) are the ones we feel are most important for students to memorize. Students should be familiar with the rest of the rules, but memorization is not required.
2. ***Copywork.** Ask students to write the grammar question, answer, and examples, if any, in the designated space in the workbook, paying attention to spelling and accuracy. **While this is a valuable learning activity, you may omit copywork if time is limited, or you may assign it for homework.* Recite aloud with students again.
3. **Exercises.** Now that students are familiar with the lesson, start the exercises. The exercises are for the purpose of further illustrating the grammar concept and developing a deeper understanding. Go over the first couple of exercises in the workbook together, and depending on the class/student, you may assign the rest as seatwork or do the whole exercise together.

   The key to understanding grammar is asking the right questions. Grammar is logical; every word or phrase in the sentence has a function. If you have the memorized terms and definitions in your mind, you should be able to discover that function by asking the right questions. This technique will be illustrated in the lessons. You should always be modeling how to **ask questions** when doing exercises.

   Check exercises immediately and correct. You should not expect mastery of grammar *application* from these exercises, nor should you assign additional exercises. The goal here is to master terms and definitions, the questions and answers. English grammar is quite abstract and cannot be mastered all at once. It is important to teach incrementally, to go through the steps. The first step is learning the concrete terms and definitions.

After the exercises, ask individual students the questions. Continue around the room until all of the students have responded to at least one question orally. Recite grammar questions and answers once a day during the week, allowing students to look at their text if necessary.

4. **Assessment: Quiz or Test.** For the quiz or test, students should be able to recite answers and examples from memory. The answer needs to be accurate in content, though not necessarily in every word.

B. Capitalization/Punctuation Rules

1. **Teach.** Write the rule with examples on the board and recite with students several times (an overhead or teaching from the text are fine). Explain the rule using the examples. Memorization of these rules is more difficult than the grammar questions and is therefore optional. You can require (a) no memorization, (b) memorization for the current week only, or (c) cumulative memorization. The latter is recommended for honors students only.
2. **Copywork.** Ask students to copy the rule and examples in the designated space in their workbook. Check to see that the examples have been copied without errors. Make corrections.
3. **Exercises.** Go over the first couple of exercises in the workbook. If students seem to understand the concept, assign the rest as seatwork. If not, do all exercises together. Check immediately and correct. Although capitalization/punctuation is not as abstract as grammar, it can be very ambiguous. Sometimes there is not necessarily one right answer.
4. **Dictation.** Dictation is an important part of these lessons. Cover the capitalization/punctuation examples for each lesson and, after reciting the rule together, dictate the examples for the student to write correctly in his workbook. Check and correct. Continue this exercise throughout the week until students can write the examples from dictation without errors. Dictation is a good warm-up for every school day.
5. **Assessment: Quiz or Test.** There are two parts to assessing capitalization/punctuation rules. The first is optional and only required if you are choosing to memorize these rules. Post the Capitalization and Punctuation Style Sheets on the wall. Cover the left half that contains the rules. The right side, with the examples, is the prompt for the rule. Read each example together and then recite the rule from memory.
   The second part, dictation, is not optional. Dictate examples for students to write on blank paper or dictation sheets. If students can't write the examples correctly, they certainly will not be able to apply the rule correctly. The unit and final assessments are cumulative, so consistent review is very important.

Review

The primary goal of review is to prepare students for each week's recitation quiz. Reciting the answers to each week's grammar questions should be well within the ability of all students.

A second review goal is the cumulative recitation at the end of each unit. You must adapt this goal to the abilities of your student(s) and the time you have allotted for review. A little review goes a long way. Most students should be able to accomplish this goal. There are two approaches to cumulative work:

1. **Choral Classroom Recitation**
   Choral classroom recitation, requiring students to master the exact wording of answers, requires more time and is a higher level of mastery. You may want to aim for this level for weekly and even unit assessments. At least once a week do a choral recitation with books open. Then close books and see how much the volume goes down.

2. **Rapid-Fire Review**
   Individual questioning around the room in a rapid-fire method is energetic and quick and may be best for cumulative grammar questions from previous units and previous years. Some students will master every question, and others will have the concept but struggle with the wording. Use these times for reteaching and review.

Recitation and Review Tips

1. Students should stand for a choral recitation, which should not exceed five minutes. Recite aloud with students, modeling enthusiasm and a strong voice. The more mastery you have over the material, the more your students will be motivated to learn. Can you say the answers while looking at your students instead of at the book? Learning goes straight from your mind to the mind of the students. The text is just an aid. In a choral recitation, usually one or two students lead the group, so you should alternate rapid-fire review questioning with choral recitation. By calling on individual students, you will have a better idea of each student's mastery.

2. For rapid-fire review questioning, you may occasionally want to divide into teams (boys/girls, Greeks/Romans, etc.) and draw questions from a basket, or use other favorite games. You can assign five review questions weekly for special attention during these sessions.

3. For "old" questions, you may need to give some help, the first few words of the answer or the examples. The initial wording is the hardest part of the answer/examples to come up with. You can also give the wording of the answer and leave the key words blank. For instance, you can say, "An adjective is a word that ________________." "A concrete noun names something that can be ________________."

4. If a student can't come up with the given example during an individual recitation, see if he can come up with his own example, which will count just as well.
5. Grammar, punctuation, and capitalization can be taught any time. Ask for the rule or grammar fact that applies in other subjects during the day.
6. Work toward mastery as best you can, first for each lesson, each unit, each year. It's all good, whatever students can master.

SUGGESTED FIVE-DAY LESSON PLAN

A full hour may be required for the first day's lesson. Days 2-5 should require no more than 5-10 minutes per day, and should consist of mastering each week's new lesson, as well as reviewing old lessons. Spread the review recitation over five days and cover as much as you can each week.

Day 1 Review Recitation
New lesson
Copywork (Optional but beneficial if time permits)
Exercises

Day 2 Review Recitation
Practice new lesson's recitation and/or dictation.

Day 3 Review Recitation
Practice new lesson's recitation and/or dictation.

Day 4 Pre-assessment—Quiz or Test (Repeat on Day 5 only if necessary.)

Day 5 Assessment

UNIT I

Workbook I & II Review

LESSON 1: Capitalization Review

REVIEW RECITATION: Turn to your style sheet in the Appendix (or use a wall chart) and recite capitalization rules and examples.

DICTATION: Cover examples and write them on blank paper from dictation.

PRACTICE A: Circle all the words that should be capitalized.

1. hear, o israel; the lord our god, the lord is one.
2. on the sixth day, god created man in his image.
3. "your classes will begin on monday, august 27," mother told me.
4. a severe drought has plagued the midwest for the second year in a row.
5. i hope mr. schaeffer will attend our next meeting.
6. i saw dr. moore at the last soccer game.
7. our first graders memorize the poem "froggies go to school."

PRACTICE B: Circle the correct phrase in each pair.

1.	1453 A.D.	1453 a.d.
2.	general Robert E. Lee	General Robert E. Lee
3.	visited the Southwest	visited the southwest
4.	your brother	your Brother
5.	a crisp Fall day	a crisp fall day
6.	722 b.c.	722 B.C.
7.	dear Alex,	Dear Alex,
8.	*The Wind in the Willows*	*the wind in the willows*
9.	governor Jim Sharp	Governor Jim Sharp
10.	driving north	driving North

PRACTICE C: Circle all words that should be capitalized.

1. the largest planet, jupiter, is named after the chief of the roman gods.
2. thousands of people traveled west to california in search of gold in 1849.
3. president thomas jefferson sent lewis and clark to explore the land west of the mississippi river.
4. a native american woman of the shoshone tribe served as their guide.
5. the explorers were to follow the missouri river to its source and gather information about plants, animals, climate, and geographical features in the louisiana territory.
6. the expedition began in st. louis, missouri, on may 4, 1804.
7. on november 7, 1805, the explorers reached the pacific ocean.
8. our family always spends labor day weekend at the colorado river.
9. which is your favorite holiday, thanksgiving or christmas?
10. the olympic games are held in a different country every four years.
11. big companies like proctor and gamble, nike, and general motors corporation help sponsor the olympic games.
12. mormon emigrants, led by brigham young, traveled west to salt lake city, utah.

QUIZ: How many examples can you write correctly from dictation? Use blank paper.

☐ Capitalization Rules #1-10 a-k Examples

LESSON 2: Punctuation Review

REVIEW RECITATION: Turn to your style sheet in the Appendix (or use a wall chart) and recite punctuation rules and examples.

☐ End Marks Rules #1-5 ☐ Comma Rules #1-4

DICTATION: Cover examples and write them on blank paper from dictation.

PRACTICE A: Add commas, punctuation, and end marks.

1. Who is the author of *Adam of the Road*
2. What a long journey Adam makes in this book
3. Please read Ch 2 for homework tonight
4. Adam and Nick are good friends
5. Adam's journey begins in June 1294 A D
6. Come on we must hurry
7. What language is spoken at St Alban's School

PRACTICE B: Draw a line through any comma used incorrectly. One sentence has two unnecessary commas, and two sentences are correct as is. Can you find them?

1. His harp, his friend, and his dog, gave Adam comfort while his father was away.
2. The British Isles include, England, Wales, Scotland, Northern Ireland, and the Republic of Ireland.
3. Perkin was a tall, thin, dark-haired boy.
4. Nick had slept with Adam, ever since he had been a small, round, wriggling, puppy.
5. Adam was not allowed to keep a dog, at the Abbey.
6. An old woman across the river, kept Nick.
7. Adam and Perkin pass through an herb garden, a vegetable garden, and an orchard on their way to Dame Malkin's cottage.
8. Nick was overjoyed, to see Adam.
9. Kings, and nobles had messengers to carry letters for them.
10. Roger pulled the boy close, bent down, and kissed him, on both cheeks.

PRACTICE C: Punctuate the letter correctly, adding commas, periods, and end marks. Underline all letters that should be capitalized.

1220 sycamore circle
atlanta georgia
november 15 2014

dear aunt sally

we are going to williamsburg the first week of may we would like for you and lucy to go with us i cant wait for lucys birthday party next friday

yours truly

billy

QUIZ: How many examples can you write correctly from dictation? Use blank paper.

☐ End Marks Rules #1-5 Examples ☐ Comma Rules #1-4 Examples

LESSON 3: Punctuation Review

REVIEW RECITATION: Turn to your style sheet in the Appendix (or use a wall chart) and recite punctuation rules and examples.

- ☐ Quotation Marks Rules #1-2
- ☐ Apostrophe Rules #1-3
- ☐ Colon Rules #1-2
- ☐ Hyphen Rules #1-2

DICTATION: Cover examples and write them on blank paper from dictation.

PRACTICE A: Rewrite the sentence, placing quotation marks and end marks where they are needed.

1. The angel said to Zacharias, Your wife shall bear you a son.

   ____

2. How can this be? Zacharias replied

   ____

3. Why can't he speak? the people asked each other

   ____

4. He shall be called Zacharias after the name of his father, they said.

   ____

5. His name is John, Zacharias wrote on a tablet

   ____

6. What kind of child shall this be! exclaimed the people of Judah.

   ____

PRACTICE B: Add an apostrophe, colon, or hyphen where needed.

1. It took thirty three years to build the London Bridge.
2. Jennifers dental appointment is at 1 30 on Thursday.
3. Great grandfather and Mother didnt want to be late.
4. The gray kittens paws are white, and the tip of its tail is also white.
5. Many pilgrims go to Bethlehem, the place of Jesus birth.
6. The eight foot board was not quite long enough to fix the fence.
7. My favorite verse is John 3 16.

QUIZ: How many examples can you write correctly from dictation? Use blank paper.

- ☐ Quotation Marks Rules #1-2 Examples
- ☐ Apostrophe Rules #1-3 Examples
- ☐ Colon Rules #1-2 Examples
- ☐ Hyphen Rules #1-2 Examples

LESSON 4: Grammar Review

REVIEW RECITATION: Grammar questions are in the Appendix or your Recitation Manual. Recite answers with examples.

☐ Grammar Questions #1-31

PRACTICE A: Give the type of sentence: *declarative, imperative, interrogative,* or *exclamatory*. Use the correct punctuation to end each sentence.

____________________ **1.** What are the different types of feathers

____________________ **2.** How complex the feather is

____________________ **3.** Feathers which reflect many colors are iridescent

____________________ **4.** Down feathers insulate birds against extreme temperatures

____________________ **5.** Find a feather and look at it under a microscope

____________________ **6.** Are all birds' feet alike

____________________ **7.** Birds are the only creatures which have feathers

____________________ **8.** Name the four basic features of birds

____________________ **9.** Talons allow birds to grip high perches and to catch prey

____________________ **10.** Did you know that over 50 species of birds do not fly

PRACTICE B: Circle the adjectives in the following sentences. Draw a line to the noun or pronoun each modifies. Remember that articles and possessive nouns and possessive pronouns are adjectives. Nouns can also function as adjectives.

1. Mother bought me a brand-new blue backpack for school.

2. I have filled it with many heavy new books and all my school supplies.

3. Our mischievous puppy chewed tiny holes in Father's socks.

4. Ann just bought some black leather boots.

5. We ate the spicy salsa with our crisp, salty chips.

6. The thirsty boys drank all the sweet, cold lemonade.

PRACTICE C: Circle the adverbs in the following sentences and underline the verbs they modify. In the blank write the question the adverb answers, *how (manner), when, where, how much.*

__________________ **1.** Michael slipped silently into his seat.

__________________ **2.** The students often ran to the park.

__________________ **3.** We will meet you here.

__________________ **4.** Mother seldom watches TV.

__________________ **5.** They usually have cookies and milk.

__________________ **6.** Beth wrote neatly in her book.

__________________ **7.** She will begin the lesson soon.

__________________ **8.** The car stopped suddenly in the middle of the road.

__________________ **9.** Paul never feeds the dog.

__________________ **10.** The children walked slowly to school.

PRACTICE D: Write three sentences below using the verb *play* in the present, the past, and the future tense.

1. Present ____

2. Past____

3. Future ____

ORAL QUIZ: Recite answers with examples:

☐ Grammar Questions #1-31

LESSON 5: Grammar Review

REVIEW RECITATION: Grammar questions are in the Appendix or your Recitation Manual. Recite answers with examples.

☐ Grammar Questions #32-57

PRACTICE A: Write the part of speech for each italicized word: *noun, verb, adjective,* or *adverb.*

__________ **1.** The ***love*** of money is the root of all evil.

__________ **2.** Christians should ***love*** the Lord their God and their neighbors.

__________ **3.** The ***table*** top is scratched and worn.

__________ **4.** The committee will ***table*** the motion until its meeting next month.

__________ **5.** Christy placed the vase of flowers on the ***table***.

__________ **6.** Mr. Myer will ***plant*** a whole field of pumpkins on his farm.

__________ **7.** That ***plant*** desperately needs water.

__________ **8.** A good captain will go ***down*** with his ship.

__________ **9.** Jim's ***down*** jacket kept him warm all winter.

PRACTICE B: Draw a line between the subject and predicate of each sentence. Underline the simple subject and circle the simple predicate.

1. Adam missed his good friend Perkin.
2. At first, Hugh and the other boys ignored Adam.
3. A small hawk, with his hooded head, perched on Simon's heavy leather glove.
4. Simon suggested that Adam share Bayard with Hugh and the other boys.
5. The boys rode Bayard at the quintain.
6. Tilting at the quintain was a game the boys played to train for jousting matches.
7. The company of six became a company of seven.
8. The boys would tilt at the quintain, swim in the river, or run footraces.
9. Sometimes Margery and Emilie joined the boys in the garden for games.

DIAGRAM: Diagram the simple subject and simple predicate for sentences 1-5 in Practice B.

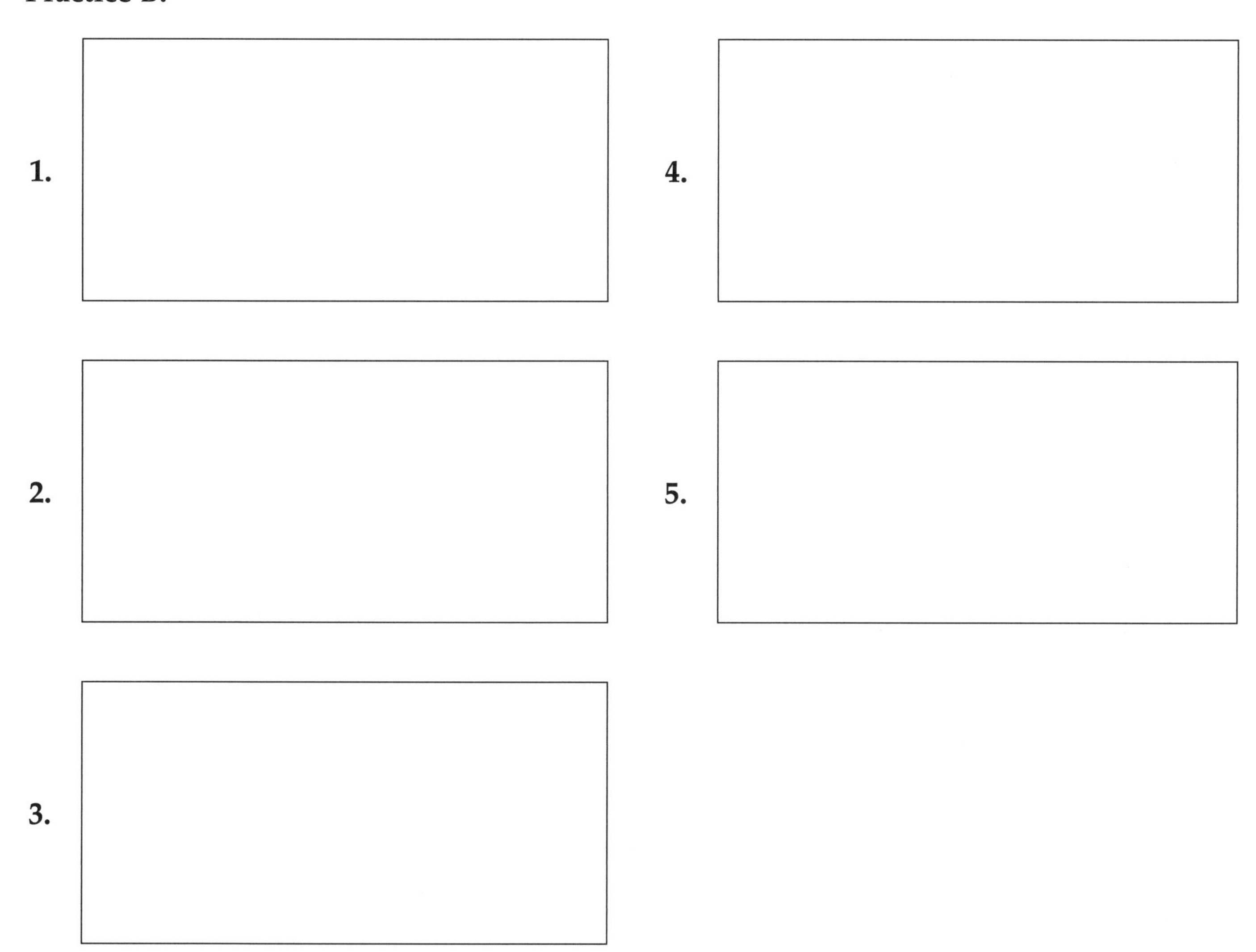

PRACTICE C: Underline the compound subject or compound verb in each sentence.

1. Football and basketball are popular American sports.
2. The sun rises in the East and sets in the West.
3. The American Goldfinch and the Yellow Warbler are two birds we have studied.
4. She took her binoculars with her and saw many different birds in the forest.
5. Sirius and Arcturus are two of the brightest stars we can see.
6. Our class will read and memorize "England's Sovereigns in Verse" this year.
7. Apples and pears ripen in the fall.
8. He picked up his harp and began to play along with the lay of Sir Orfeo.
9. Adam and Nick rode in the carriage.
10. Math and science are my favorite subjects.

DIAGRAM: Diagram the subject and verb for sentences 6-9 in Practice C.

6.

8.

7.

9.

PRACTICE D: Fill in the correct past form of the regular and irregular verbs in parentheses.

1. The angel Gabriel ______________ to tell Mary of God's plan. (come)
2. After she heard the news, Mary ______________ to visit Elizabeth. (go)
3. Elizabeth ___________ Mary coming and greeted her joyfully. (see)
4. Mary ___________ Elizabeth what the angel had said to her. (tell)
5. Zacharias __________ "His name is John" on a tablet. (write)
6. Caesar Augustus __________ out a decree that all the world should be taxed. (send)
7. Joseph __________ what was required of him by the law. (do)
8. Joseph __________ with Mary to Bethlehem, the city of David. (go)
9. And so, Jesus was ______________ in Bethlehem of Judea. (be born)
10. Shepherds _________ and worshiped the new-born King. (come)

PRACTICE E: Give the four principal parts for each of the following verbs.

Infinitive	Present Participle	Past	Past Participle
to stay			
		brought	
	kicking		
to speak			
			have sung

PRACTICE F: Underline the verb or verb phrase in each of the following sentences. Circle the participle and draw an arrow to the word the participle modifies. Give the verb the participle is formed from.

1. The struggling swimmer returned to the shore.

2. The defeated team left the arena quickly.

3. The injured player returned to the locker room.

4. Filled to the rafters with fans, the gym was very loud.

5. Jacob, surrounded by fans, set off for the game.

PRACTICE G: Underline the complete verb (the main verb and its helping verbs) in each sentence. Draw a line from each sentence to the correct tense form. Review progressive and emphatic forms first, Grammar Questions # 47-52.

Past	**1.** He is learning Spanish.
Past perfect	**2.** He did learn Spanish last year.
Past emphatic	**3.** He was learning Spanish a year ago.
Past progressive	**4.** He learns Spanish easily.
Present	**5.** He learned Spanish easily.
Present perfect	**6.** He has learned Spanish easily.
Present emphatic	**7.** He will learn Spanish next year.
Present progressive	**8.** He does learn Spanish easily.
Future	**9.** He will be learning Spanish next year.
Future perfect	**10.** He had learned Spanish before he learned French.
Future progressive	**11.** He will have learned Spanish by the end of the year.

ORAL QUIZ: Recite answers with examples:

☐ Grammar Questions #32-57

UNIT I REVIEW

REVIEW RECITATION: Review all capitalization/punctuation rules and grammar questions from this review unit.

PRACTICE A: Circle the words in the following sentences that should be capitalized.

1. aunt marie told us the story of how our grandfather came to new york from italy.
2. we will begin reading *a door in the wall* in november.
3. "your piano lessons have been moved to tuesday afternoon," mother said.
4. thursday is named after the teuton god thor.
5. president woodrow wilson tried to keep america out of world war I.
6. british, irish, dutch, and german immigrants came to america in large numbers in the early 1900s.
7. do all christian religions celebrate the birth of jesus christ at christmas?
8. the first u.s. post office west of the alleghenies was built in danville, kentucky.
9. james has earned the life scout award with the boy scouts of america.
10. in june, mr. john jones bought a john deere tractor for his farm.

PRACTICE B: Underline the adjectives in the following sentences. Do not underline any articles. Indicate whether the adjective tells *which one, what kind,* and *how much* or *how many.*

_________________ 1. Sir Gervase de Warenne was a burly, red-faced man.

_________________ 2. Simon waited for seven years.

_________________ 3. Adam wrote a tune for those words.

_________________ 4. A fire blazed in the hearth on cold days.

_________________ 5. Line the chairs up along that wall.

_________________ 6. Emilie was a beautiful young lady.

PRACTICE C: Add an adverb to the following sentences that answer the questions indicated.

1. The minstrel played _____________ for the lord of the manor. (How often)
2. He played his harp _____________. (How or manner)
3. They had to leave _____________ after the wedding. (When)
4. The dog waited _____________ for his master. (Where)

PRACTICE D: Underline the verbs or verb phrases in the following sentences. Tell whether each verb or verb phrase is *past, present,* or *future* tense.

_____________ 1. The Vandals, a Germanic people, settled in Spain and North Africa.

_____________ 2. Their king, Genseric, will attack Rome several times.

_____________ 3. The Vandals completely destroy the cities they conquer.

_____________ 4. "Vandal" now means a person who damages or destroys property.

_____________ 5. Genseric and the Vandals conquered the town of Hippo.

_____________ 6. They also plundered many towns along the Mediterranean coast.

_____________ 7. Maximus will flee the city of Rome when he hears about the Vandals.

_____________ 8. None of the Roman emperors stopped the Vandals.

TEST: How many grammar questions can you answer correctly with examples?

☐ Grammar Questions #1-31

☐ Grammar Questions #32-57

UNIT II
SENTENCE COMPLEMENTS

LESSON 6: Sentence Complements

REVIEW RECITATION:

☐ Grammar Questions #34-35

LESSON:

***Grammar Question #58:** What is a sentence complement? Give the four complements.

*A **complement** is one or more words in the predicate that complete the meaning of the subject and verb. The four complements are **predicate nominative**, **predicate adjective**, **direct object**, and **indirect object**.*

Grammar Question #59: What parts of speech are NOT complements?
Adverbs and prepositional phrases are not complements.

Ex. 1 Wilbur walks **in the barn**. (prepositional phrase)

Ex. 2 Wilbur walks **slowly**. (adverb)

COPYWORK:

Grammar Question #58: ______________________________

____

Answer: ______________________________

____

____

____

____

Grammar Question #59: ______________________________

____

Answer: ______________________________

____

Ex. 1 ______________________________

Ex. 2 ______________________________

PRACTICE A: Underline the verb or verb phrase in each sentence. Draw a line between the subject and predicate. Remember that the line will usually come right before the verb. Ask "What (or who)?" after the subject and verb. Circle the complement.

1. Lassie was a collie.
2. Peter bought a pocket knife.
3. Father is driving the tractor.
4. Mary will visit our great-grandmother.
5. She opened the gate.
6. Aaron wears his raincoat and boots on rainy days.
7. Mother is happy on sunny days.
8. They planted tomatoes and green beans.
9. His favorite dessert is chocolate chip ice cream.
10. We will be reading *The Wind in the Willows* next year.

PRACTICE B: Ask "What?" after the subject and verb to find the complement, and then circle it. For the two sentences that don't have complements, write either *prepositional phrase* or *adverb* out to the side.

1. The mailman delivered the mail.
2. Our grandfather is a carpenter and a farmer.
3. The children were happy.
4. Snowdrops and crocuses are flowers.
5. David slept soundly.
6. He made his bed.
7. David and Michael finished their chores.
8. They fed the chickens and the goats.
9. Mother cleans on Mondays.
10. He is learning Spanish.

ORAL QUIZ: Recite answers with examples.

☐ Grammar Questions #58-59

LESSON 7: Predicate Nominatives and Adjectives

REVIEW RECITATION:

☐ Grammar Questions #24-29, 58-59

LESSON:

***Grammar Question #60:** Define predicate nominative. Give an example.

*A **predicate nominative** is a noun or pronoun that follows a **linking verb** and renames the subject.*

Ex. Wilbur is a **pig**.

***Grammar Question #61:** Define predicate adjective. Give an example.

*A **predicate adjective** is an adjective that follows a **linking verb** and modifies the subject.*

Ex. Wilbur is **tired**.

COPYWORK:

Grammar Question #60: ______________________________

Answer: ______________________________

____

Ex. ______________________________

Grammar Question #61: ______________________________

Answer: ______________________________

____

Ex. ______________________________

PRACTICE A: Underline the verb or verb phrase and draw a line between the subject and predicate. Ask "What?" after the subject and verb, and then circle the complements. Write *predicate nominative* or *predicate adjective* for each sentence.

______________ **1.** They are strong and wise.

______________ **2.** The apple pie is wonderful.

______________ **3.** He is a man of valor.

______________ **4.** Mrs. White was my second grade teacher.

______________ **5.** The honeybees were busy from sunrise to sundown.

______________ **6.** The gate to eternal life is narrow.

______________ **7.** Francois Huber was a blind naturalist.

______________ **8.** Faith is the substance of things hoped for.

PRACTICE B: Complete each of the following sentences with a predicate nominative.

1. James is ______________________________.
2. When I grow up, I will become a ______________________________.
3. George Washington was ______________________________.
4. An ugly caterpillar can become ______________________________.
5. My favorite dessert is ______________________________.

DIAGRAM: Diagram the simple subject, simple predicate, and predicate nominative for sentences 1, 5 in Practice B. See Appendix for diagramming guidelines.

1.

5.

PRACTICE C: Complete each of the following sentences with a predicate adjective.

1. The puppies are ______________________________.
2. The freshly baked bread is ______________________________.
3. The houses were ______________________________.
4. I am ______________________________.
5. My old stuffed animal was______________________________.

DIAGRAM: Diagram the simple subject, simple predicate, and predicate adjective for sentences 1-2 in Practice C.

1.

2.

ORAL QUIZ: Recite answers with examples.

☐ Grammar Questions #60-61

LESSON 8: Linking Verbs

REVIEW RECITATION:

☐ Grammar Questions #58-61

LESSON:

***Grammar Question #62:** What question does the predicate nominative or predicate adjective answer?
*The predicate nominative or adjective answers the question **what** or **who** after a **linking** verb.*

***Grammar Question #63:** What is a linking verb?
*A **linking verb** connects the subject with a noun or adjective in the predicate. It shows **being**, not action.*

***Grammar Question #64:** What is the most common linking verb?
*The **to be** verb is the most common linking verb.*

Grammar Question #65: Forms of the *to be* verb may be used as linking verbs or helping verbs. Give an example of each.

Ex. 1 Wilbur **is** a pig. (linking verb)

Ex. 2 Wilbur **is walking** to the barn. (helping verb for main verb, *walking*)

COPYWORK:

Grammar Question #62: ____________________

____

Answer: ____________________

____

Grammar Question #63: ____________________

Answer: ____________________

____

Grammar Question #64: ____________________

Answer: ____________________

Grammar Question #65: ____________________

____

Ex. 1 ____________________

Ex. 2 ____________________

For Practice A and B: Underline the verb phrase and indicate in the space provided whether the *to be* verb is a *linking* or a *helping* verb. If linking verb, circle the complement, and to the right, tell if it is a *predicate nominative* or a *predicate adjective*.

PRACTICE A:

________________ 1. Grandfather is making cheese from the goat's milk.

________________ 2. Peter is unhappy about going to school in the winter.

________________ 3. Peter's Grannie was blind.

________________ 4. Heidi's aunt is taking her away from Grandfather.

________________ 5. Clara is an invalid who needs a playmate.

________________ 6. Heidi and Clara were very good friends.

________________ 7. She is searching for the fir trees.

________________ 8. Heidi was always getting into trouble.

PRACTICE B:

________________ 1. The giant sequoia and the California redwood are giant trees.

________________ 2. We were walking through the redwood forest in the Sierra Nevada Mountains.

________________ 3. Both the sugar maple and sweetgum are trees which produce sweet sap.

________________ 4. We were eating delicious pancakes with fresh maple syrup.

________________ 5. The mighty oak was once a tiny acorn.

________________ 6. Mark is hiking the Appalachian Mountain trails.

________________ 7. This seedling will be a giant sequoia one day.

________________ 8. Trees are important to us in many different ways.

DIAGRAM: Diagram the simple subject, predicate, and complement for sentences 3 and 5 in Practice A. See Appendix for diagramming guidelines.

3.

5.

ORAL QUIZ: Recite answers with examples.

☐ Grammar Questions #62-65

LESSON 9: Linking Verbs

REVIEW RECITATION:

☐ Grammar Questions #58-65

LESSON:

Grammar Question #66: What verbs in addition to the *to be* verb can be linking verbs?
appear, become, feel, grow, look, remain, seem, smell, sound, stay, taste

Grammar Question #67: Use *smell* as an action verb and a linking verb.
Jane ***smells*** *the rose.* (action verb)
The rose ***smells*** *wonderful.* (linking verb)

Substitute "is" (am/are) for the verb to determine if it is an action or a linking verb. Your substitution will only make sense when it is a linking verb. (*The rose is wonderful* makes sense. *Jane is the rose* does not make sense.)

COPYWORK:

Grammar Question #66: ______________________________

____

Answer: ______________________________

____

Grammar Question #67: ______________________________

____

Answer: ______________________________

____

PRACTICE A: Underline the verb or verb phrase. Tell if it is a linking verb or an action verb. Remember, you can substitute "is" (am, are) for the verb to determine if it is a *linking* or an *action verb*.

________ **1.** Edmund felt slightly sick after the long car ride.

________ **2.** He felt the icy cold water in the stream.

________ **3.** The sky grew dark and threatening.

________ **4.** Grandmother grows beautiful roses in her garden.

________ **5.** Kim has become an excellent volleyball player.

________ **6.** Everyone stayed calm during the fire drill.

________ **7.** Sam appeared very nervous before the first game.

________ **8.** You seem very tired after your trip.

________________ **9.** The steady rain sounded quite soothing to the farmer.

________________ **10.** She sounded a bell when it was time to come to class.

PRACTICE B: Insert a linking verb into each sentence. You may use a form of the *to be* verb only once.

1. The spring air ________________ fresh and clean after the rain.

2. The audience ________________ seated after the performance ended.

3. Tammy ________________ exhausted after working in the garden all day.

4. Your freshly baked blueberry pie ________________ wonderful!

5. Our teacher ________________ pleased with our success.

6. He ________________ ready to play the game.

7. The freshly cut bouquet of flowers ________________ fragrant.

8. The limerick ________________ very silly to him.

9. Peter ________________ truly sorry for what he had done.

10. That book ________________ very valuable to him.

DIAGRAM: Diagram the simple subject, predicate, and complement for sentences 1, 3, 6, and 7 in Practice A. See Appendix for diagramming guidelines.

1.

6.

3.

7.

ORAL QUIZ: Recite answers with examples.

☐ Grammar Questions #66-67

LESSON 10: Direct Objects

REVIEW RECITATION: ☐ Grammar Questions #58-67

LESSON:

***Grammar Question #68:** Define direct object. Give an example.
*A **direct object** is a noun or pronoun that receives the action of the verb.*

Ex. The magister teaches **Latin**.

***Grammar Question #69:** What question does a direct object answer?
*The direct object answers the question **what** or **whom** after an **action** verb.*

COPYWORK:

Grammar Question #68: ______________________________

Answer: ______________________________

____

Ex. ______________________________

Grammar Question #69: ______________________________

Answer: ______________________________

____

PRACTICE A: Underline the verb and draw a vertical line between the subject and predicate. Ask yourself, "What?" after the subject and verb to find the direct object, and circle it.

1. Constantine had a vision of an enormous cross of fire.
2. He had a dream about Christ's promise of victory.
3. Constantine made the standard in the form of a cross.
4. Constantine made Christianity legal.
5. He made important improvements in the Roman laws and government.
6. Constantine expanded the Roman Empire.
7. He moved the capital from Rome to Byzantium.
8. He built beautiful buildings.
9. He constructed streets and public squares.
10. He renamed the city Constantinople.

DIAGRAM: Diagram the simple subject, the simple predicate, and the direct object for sentences 2, 3, 7, and 8 in Practice A. See Appendix for diagramming guidelines.

2.

7.

3.

8.

PRACTICE B: Underline the verb and draw a vertical line between the subject and predicate. Ask yourself, "What?" after the subject and verb to find the complement, and circle it. Tell whether the complement is a *direct object, pred. nom.,* or *pred. adj.*

____________ **1.** The children made a snowman the next morning.

____________ **2.** The children were cold.

____________ **3.** The snow felt soft and fluffy.

____________ **4.** Peter and John have built a fort out of snow.

____________ **5.** The boys threw snowballs at each other.

____________ **6.** Father was the referee in the game.

____________ **7.** The snowman grew smaller.

____________ **8.** Mother scolded them for tracking mud and snow into the house.

____________ **9.** The warm sunshine melted the snowman the next day.

____________ **10.** The snow looked beautiful in the bright sunlight.

ORAL QUIZ: Recite answers with examples.

☐ Grammar Questions #68-69

LESSON 11: Complementary Infinitive

REVIEW RECITATION:

☐ Grammar Questions #37-39, 58-69

LESSON:

Grammar Question #70: What is a complementary infinitive? Give an example.
A complementary infinitive is an infinitive used as a direct object.

Ex. Wilbur loves **to learn**. Wilbur wants **to eat**.

COPYWORK:

Grammar Question #70: ______________________________

____

Answer: ______________________________

____

Ex. ______________________________

____

PRACTICE A: Underline the verb or verb phrase in each sentence. Circle the infinitive.

1. The old woman wished to call the dog back to her.
2. The kind old couple had decided to give Lassie her freedom.
3. Rowlie Palmer attempted to feed Lassie.
4. She had learned to eat only from a bowl or plate.
5. Lassie wants to travel south.
6. Lassie returned to help Rowlie.
7. The two men tried to retreat from Lassie's attacks.
8. Lassie attempts to cross the moor in heavy snowfall.
9. Lassie loved to meet Joe at the school gate.
10. Lassie was determined to see her home again.

PRACTICE B: Write a sentence using a complementary infinitive along with each verb below. Remember the infinitive must answer the question "What?" of the action verb.

1. want ____

____

2. love ____

____

3. hope ____

____

4. learn ____

____

5. plan ____

____

DIAGRAM: Diagram sentences 5-8 in Practice A. See Appendix for diagramming guidelines.

5.

6.

7.

8.

ORAL QUIZ: Recite answers with examples.

☐ Grammar Question #70

LESSON 12: Indirect Objects

REVIEW RECITATION: ☐ Grammar Questions #58-70

LESSON:

***Grammar Question #71:** What is an indirect object? Give an example.
*The **indirect object** precedes the direct object and tells to whom or for whom the action of the verb is done.*

Ex. 1 The magister teaches **me** Latin.

Ex. 2 The magister gives **John** a test.

Grammar Question #72: What kind of verbs usually have indirect objects?
Giving and telling verbs usually have indirect objects.

COPYWORK:

Grammar Question #71: ____________________

Answer: ____________________

____

Ex. 1 ____________________

Ex. 2 ____________________

Grammar Question #72: ____________________

____

Answer: ____________________

PRACTICE A: Underline the verb or verb phrase once and the direct object twice. Ask yourself, "To or for whom/what?" of the verb and direct object to find the indirect object. Circle the indirect object.

1. Mrs. Fadden served him a cup of hot tea.
2. The waiter brought them a delicious steak dinner.
3. Father will buy me some new running shoes.
4. Bruce showed the class his coin collection.
5. Ann fed her horse fine timothy hay.
6. The White Witch gave Edmund Turkish Delight.
7. Lucy gave Mr. Tumnus a handkerchief.
8. Schools should teach children logic.
9. Father Christmas gives Susan an ivory horn.

PRACTICE B: Rewrite each by turning the *to/for* prepositional phrase into an indirect object.

1. The farmer fed grain to the geese.______________________________

2. We bought a bouquet of flowers for Mother. ______________________________

3. Mrs. Brown is giving a gift to Mark.______________________________

4. The magister teaches Latin to her. ______________________________

5. Dan gave a bone to the dog.______________________________

DIAGRAM: Diagram the simple subject, simple predicate, direct object, and indirect object for each sentence in Practice B. See Appendix for diagramming guidelines.

1.

2.

3.

4.

5.

ORAL QUIZ: Recite answers with examples.

☐ Grammar Questions #71-72

UNIT II REVIEW: Sentence Complements

REVIEW RECITATION:

☐ Grammar Questions #58-72

PRACTICE A: Underline the verb or verb phrase in each sentence. Draw a line between the subject and predicate. Circle the complement, and tell whether it is a *predicate nominative* or *predicate adjective*.

______________________ 1. Lassie grew strong again, thanks to Dan and Dally.

______________________ 2. Dan and Dally Fadden were an elderly couple.

______________________ 3. Animals are creatures of habit.

______________________ 4. Lassie looked beautiful after Dan cleaned her up.

______________________ 5. She became restless and agitated each day around four.

______________________ 6. The dog seems too polite to run away.

______________________ 7. The tea was growing cold.

______________________ 8. The warm milk tasted sweet to Lassie.

______________________ 9. Rowlie was a small, cheery man.

______________________ 10. He was a traveling potter.

PRACTICE B: Underline the verb or verb phrase in each sentence below and circle the direct object.

1. The Johnson family eats dinner at 6 o'clock.
2. Our class visited the zoo last week.
3. Danny always plays baseball in the summer.
4. He practices his pitching and hitting with his father.
5. John Chapman planted apple trees all across the Midwest.
6. The boys will wash the cars this afternoon.
7. Susan received the beautiful bouquet of flowers.
8. A mole dug tunnels all over the front lawn.

PRACTICE C: Underline the verb or verb phrase in each sentence. Draw a line between the subject and predicate. Indicate whether the verb is an *action verb* or a *linking verb*. Circle the complement if there is one. Two sentences don't have a complement.

____________________ 1. Only one queen bee rules a hive.

____________________ 2. The upholster bee and the mason bee do not live in hives.

____________________ 3. The honey bee carries pollen in a "basket" on its legs.

____________________ 4. Bees are industrious little insects.

____________________ 5. Every bee in the hive has a job to do.

____________________ 6. The worker bee is hardworking.

____________________ 7. A queen bee will fly away from her old hive.

____________________ 8. Honeybees help farmers and gardeners by pollinating plants.

____________________ 9. The Word of God is sweeter than honey from the honeycomb.

____________________ 10. The drone is the laziest bee in the hive.

PRACTICE D: Underline the verb or verb phrase in the following sentences once, and underline the direct object twice. Ask yourself, "To or for whom/what?" of the verb and direct object to find the indirect object. Circle the indirect object.

1. We will give the Jones family our old car.
2. Mrs. Williams is teaching us long division.
3. John gave the mechanic fifty dollars.
4. Mother would read us stories every night after dinner.
5. He didn't tell us his plans.
6. Please give me time to finish my chores.

PRACTICE E: Underline the verb or verb phrase and circle the complementary infinitive. In one sentence the infinitive is the subject. Can you find it?

1. We will try to memorize the first three stanzas of the poem.
2. Would you like to join the swim team?
3. Mark began to paint the deck this morning.
4. He failed to finish the job before dark.
5. To win a gold medal is the dream of many Olympic athletes.
6. Peter is learning to speak Spanish.
7. He hopes to go on a mission trip to Guadalajara next summer.

DIAGRAM: Diagram the simple subject, simple predicate, direct object, and indirect object for each sentence listed below. See Appendix for diagramming guidelines.

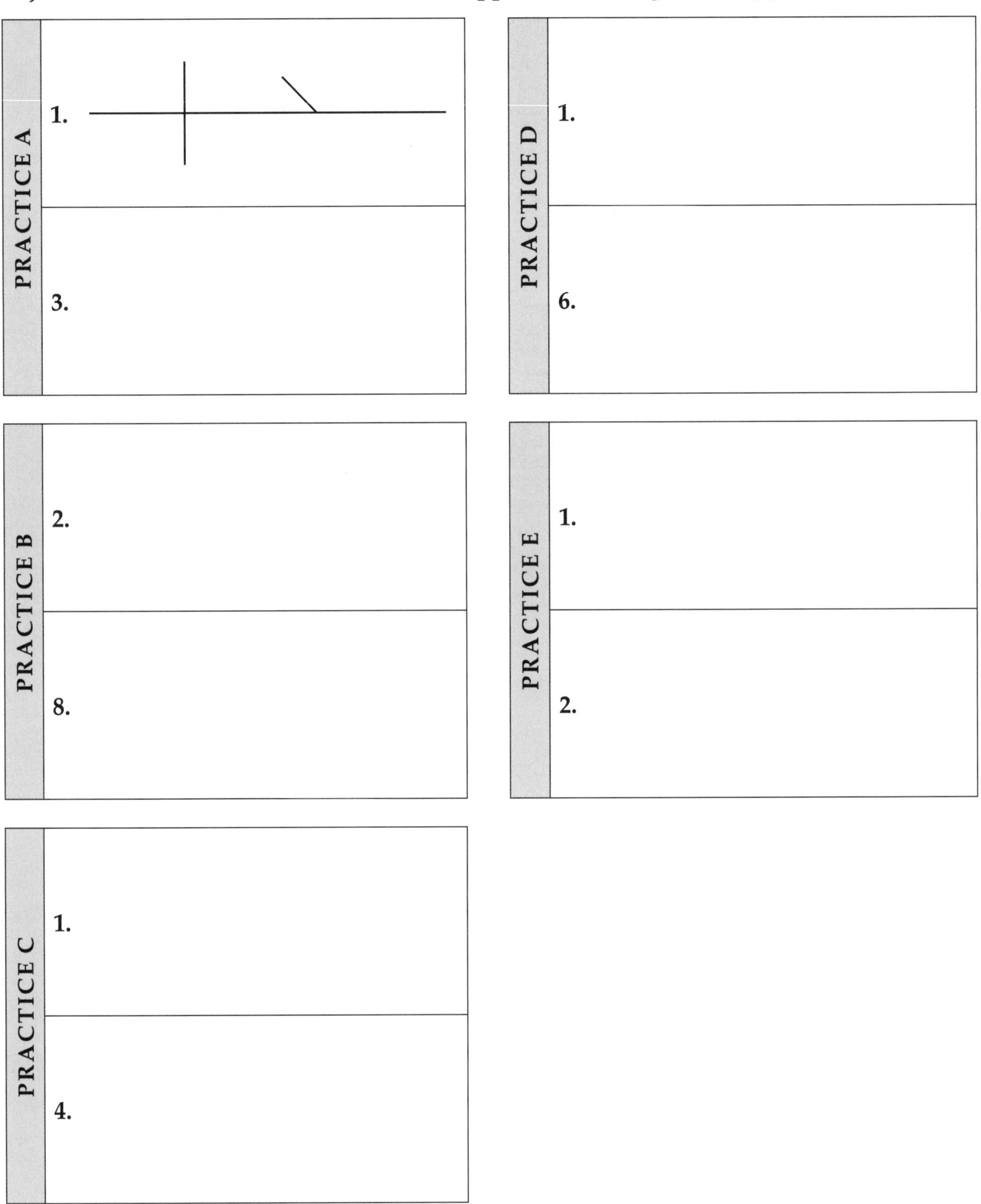

TEST: How many grammar questions with examples can you answer correctly?

☐ Grammar Questions #58-72

UNIT III

Sentences, Pronouns, & Capitalization

LESSON 13: Finding the Subject

REVIEW RECITATION:

☐ Grammar Questions #3, 32-36

LESSON:

Grammar Question #73: Give five difficulties in finding the subject, with examples.

a. *In sentences expressing a command or request, the subject is always **you**.*

Ex. Study your Latin.
(You) Study your Latin.

b. *To find a subject in a question, turn the question into a statement.*

Ex. What lesson did you study? (question)
You did study what lesson. (statement)
Subject: *You*; Verb: *did study*

c. *The subject of a sentence is never a prepositional phrase.*

Ex. **Neither** of the students **studied** his Latin.
Neither is the subject. *Students* is the object of the preposition *of*.

COPYWORK:

Grammar Question #73: ______________________________

a. ______________________________

Ex. ______________________________

____

b. ______________________________

Ex. ______________________________

____

c. ______________________________

Ex. ______________________________

PRACTICE A: Rewrite the following commands or requests, adding the unstated subject *you* in parentheses. The first one is done for you.

1. Jason, rake the leaves. Jason, (you) rake the leaves.
2. Carrie, fold the clothes. (you) ______________________________
3. Stand up and recite the poem. ______________________________
4. Don't fall in the lake. ______________________________
5. Taste this delicious cake. ______________________________

PRACTICE B: Rewrite the following questions as declarative statements. Then circle the subject of the new sentence.

1. What clothes did Anna take on her trip? ______________________________

____

2. Are you going to adopt a dog? ______________________________

____

3. What spice do you taste in this bread? ______________________________

____

4. Which countries are found in North America? ______________________________

____

5. Are you staying after school for track practice? ______________________________

____

PRACTICE C: Underline the verb or verb phrase in each sentence below. Ask yourself, "Who or what?" before the verb to find the subject, and circle it. Remember, the object of a preposition cannot be the subject.

1. Each of the boys had a guilty look on his face.
2. Neither of them admitted to breaking the vase.
3. Both of the boys cleaned up the shattered glass.
4. Most of the chocolate chip cookies have been eaten.
5. Everyone in our family loves freshly baked chocolate chip cookies.
6. Several of the cookies were very crispy.

ORAL QUIZ: Recite answers with examples.

☐ Grammar Question #73 a-c

LESSON 14: Finding the Subject

REVIEW RECITATION:

☐ Grammar Question #73 a-c

LESSON:

Grammar Question #73: Give five difficulties in finding the subject, with examples.

d. ***Here*** *is not usually the subject of a verb.*

Ex. Here is the book.

The **book** is here. (reworded)

Here is an adverb telling where. *Book* is the subject of the verb *is*.

e. *The expletives* ***there*** *and* ***it*** *are not usually subjects of a verb.*

Ex. 1 **There** are books on both tables.

Books are on both tables. (reworded)

Books is the subject of the verb *are*. *There* gets the sentence started.

Ex. 2 **It** is important to study Latin.

To study Latin is important. (reworded)

To study is the subject of the verb *is*. *It* gets the sentence started.

An **expletive** is a word with no grammatical function.

COPYWORK:

Grammar Question #73: ____________________

d. ____________________

Ex. ____________________

____

e. ____________________

Ex. 1 ____________________

____

Ex. 2 ____________________

____

PRACTICE A: Rewrite to find the subject. Circle subject.

1. Here is a beautiful valley! ______________________________

____

2. There are many books on my shelves. ______________________________

____

3. It is a good idea to do your homework. ______________________________

____

4. Here is my homework. ______________________________

____

5. There are clothes in the washer. ______________________________

____

6. It is not advisable to miss school. ______________________________

____

PRACTICE B: Rewrite to find the subject. Circle subject. Write (You) at the beginning of the sentence if it is the unstated subject.

1. Look closely at the blue jay's feather. ______________________________

____

2. Does the feather always look blue? ______________________________

____

3. Here are several cardinal and goldfinch feathers. ______________________________

____

4. Listen carefully to the female cardinal's song. ______________________________

____

5. Do the birds have different types of bills? ______________________________

____

ORAL QUIZ: Recite answers with examples.

☐ Grammar Question #73 a-e

LESSON 15: Pronouns

REVIEW RECITATION:

☐ Grammar Questions #15-18, 73

LESSON:

***Grammar Question #74:** Give the eight kinds of pronouns in pairs.
Personal and Possessive (See Rules, 76-77)
Intensive and Reflexive (See Rules 104-106)
Relative and Interrogative (See Rules 128-131)
Demonstrative and Indefinite (See Rules 107-108, 132)

Grammar Question #75: Many pronouns can also function as what part of speech?
Many pronouns also function as adjectives.

COPYWORK:

Grammar Question #74: ______________________________

____

Answer: ______________________________

____

____

____

Grammar Question #75: ______________________________

____

Answer: ______________________________

____

PRACTICE A: Underline and identify the kind of pronoun.

_______________ 1. Mary gave me a rose from Mother's favorite rosebush.

_______________ 2. All of the roses are in bloom now.

_______________ 3. Mother herself planted the rosebush last spring.

_______________ 4. The children left their dishes on the table.

_______________ 5. Sam is the one who washed all the dishes.

_______________ 6. Will Charles read all these today?

_______________ 7. What is Tom's favorite flavor of ice cream?

_______________ 8. John helped himself to a second piece of cake.

_______________ 9. You have worked hard in the garden today.

_______________ 10. The injured dog licked its wounds.

PRACTICE B: Underline and identify the kind of pronoun. Tell whether it is used as an adjective or a pronoun.

_______________ 1. Tony carried his suitcase to the station.

_______________ 2. Mine already has a hole in the sole.

_______________ 3. Anyone can play the game.

_______________ 4. Few people will be able to come.

_______________ 5. Have the students read these yet?

_______________ 6. Is that street always busy?

_______________ 7. Who will finish the lesson first?

_______________ 8. What time is the game tomorrow?

_______________ 9. Mark knows which soccer cleats are best.

_______________ 10. Charles has a suit that fits him well.

ORAL QUIZ: Recite answers.

☐ Grammar Questions #74-75

LESSON 16: Possessive Pronouns

REVIEW RECITATION:

☐ Grammar Questions #73-75

LESSON:

Grammar Question #76: Give the pronoun forms of the possessive pronoun.
mine, yours, his, hers, its, ours, yours, theirs

Grammar Question #77: Give the adjective forms of the possessive pronoun.
my, your, his, her, its, our, your, their

COPYWORK:

Grammar Question #76: ______________________________

____

Answer: ______________________________

Grammar Question #77: ______________________________

____

Answer: ______________________________

PRACTICE A: Underline the possessive pronouns in the following sentences. Tell whether the pronoun is in its *pronoun* or *adjective* form.

______________ **1.** The cookbooks on the table are hers.

______________ **2.** Her cookbooks are on the table.

______________ **3.** The tools in the garage are his.

______________ **4.** Are his tools in the garage?

______________ **5.** My house is two blocks from the school.

______________ **6.** The first suitcase taken off the plane was mine.

______________ **7.** Yours is the best project at the science fair.

______________ **8.** Wash your hands before you eat your lunch.

______________ **9.** Their coats are hanging in the hall closet.

______________ **10.** Are all of these boots theirs?

PRACTICE B: Fill in the blank with the correct corresponding possessive pronoun for the words in parentheses.

1. Tony carried _________ suitcase to the station. (suitcase belonging to Tony)
2. Father raised many vegetables in _________ garden. (Father's garden)
3. There are many bedrooms in _________ old house. (house belonging to us)
4. Both of _________ shoes have holes in them! (shoes belonging to me)
5. We will wash _________ car on Saturday, Mother. (car belonging to Mother)
6. The water of the creek overflowed _________ banks. (banks of creek)
7. You must turn in _________ research paper today. (paper belonging to you)
8. Mary spilled grape juice on _________ new white dress. (dress belonging to Mary)
9. The baby birds fell out of _________ nest. (nest of the birds)
10. The huge oak tree lost all of _________ leaves in the winter. (leaves of the tree)

ORAL QUIZ: Recite answers.

☐ Grammar Questions #76-77

LESSON 17: Transitive and Intransitive Verbs

REVIEW RECITATION:

☐ Grammar Questions #68-69, 73-77

LESSON:

***Grammar Question #78:** What is a **transitive** verb? Give examples.
*A **transitive** verb requires a direct object to complete its meaning.*

Ex. 1 John ignored the insult.

Ex. 2 John completed his lesson.

***Grammar Question #79:** What is an **intransitive** verb? Give examples.
*An **intransitive** verb does not require a direct object to complete its meaning.*

Ex. **Sleep, laugh, look, die,** and the **to be** verb are always intransitive.

***Grammar Question #80:** Many verbs can be used both transitively and intransitively. Give examples.

Ex. 1 I eat pizza. transitive, *pizza* is a direct object

Ex. 2 I eat every day. intransitive, *every day* is an adverb, not a direct object

COPYWORK: Complete on a separate sheet of paper.

PRACTICE A: Underline the verb or verb phrase in each sentence. If the verb has a direct object, circle it and write *transitive* in the blank. If there is not a d.o., write *intransitive* in the blank.

______________________ **1.** Roger plays the piano.

______________________ **2.** He plays beautifully.

______________________ **3.** Jenny tasted the mango.

______________________ **4.** The mango is very sweet.

______________________ **5.** The soccer players ran twelve laps.

______________________ **6.** George ran faster than the other boys.

______________________ **7.** Matt is studying Latin this year.

______________________ **8.** He is studying diligently.

______________________ **9.** A minstrel lived a life of travel and adventure.

______________________ **10.** My grandfather lives with us now.

PRACTICE B: In each pair of sentences, one verb is transitive and one is intransitive. For the transitive verb, write *transitive* and give the direct object. For the *intransitive* verb, underline the adverb or adverb prepositional phrase and write the question the adverb answers. The first one is done for you.

1. Intransitive – when? ______ The boys played <u>after dark</u>.
   Transitive – kickball ______ The boys played kickball.
2. ______________________ Joe ate a hamburger.
   ______________________ Joe ate eagerly.
3. ______________________ The people watched with great interest.
   ______________________ The people watched the show.
4. ______________________ You will study geography next year.
   ______________________ You will study hard.
5. ______________________ John read quietly.
   ______________________ John read *The Hobbit*.
6. ______________________ Adam ran yesterday.
   ______________________ Adam ran the race.
7. ______________________ Roger traveled the roads of England.
   ______________________ Roger traveled all night.
8. ______________________ Anna walked carefully across the bridge.
   ______________________ Anna walked the dog.
9. ______________________ My mother calls me.
   ______________________ My mother calls daily.

ORAL QUIZ: Recite answers with examples.

☐ Grammar Questions #78-80

LESSON 18: Active and Passive Voice

REVIEW RECITATION:

☐ Grammar Questions #73-80

LESSON:

***Grammar Question #81:** What is the difference between the active and passive voice?
*In the **active** voice, the subject performs the action of the verb. In the **passive** voice, the subject receives the action of the verb.*

COPYWORK:

Grammar Question #81: ____

____

Answer: ____

____

____

PRACTICE A: Find the subject and verb of each sentence. Ask yourself if the subject is performing or receiving the action of the verb. For each pair of sentences, identify which is in the *passive* voice and which is in the *active*.

____________________ **1.** Mary washed the floors.

____________________ **2.** The floors were washed yesterday.

____________________ **3.** The cows are fed hay every day.

____________________ **4.** Henry feeds the cows.

____________________ **5.** We are given grace by the Lord Jesus Christ.

____________________ **6.** God gives us grace to do what is right.

____________________ **7.** We are strengthened by adversity.

____________________ **8.** Adversity develops strong character.

____________________ **9.** The Smiths like desserts with their meals.

____________________ **10.** All of the desserts were eaten at the picnic.

PRACTICE B: Underline the verb or verb phrase in each sentence. Ask yourself if the subject is performing or receiving the action of the verb. Tell whether the verb is in the *active* or *passive* voice.

________________ **1.** Charles rode his bicycle to George's house.

________________ **2.** The ball was kicked into the corner of the soccer goal.

________________ **3.** Mary prepared a delicious meal.

________________ **4.** A nutritious lunch is prepared for us daily.

________________ **5.** The moth was caught by the bird.

________________ **6.** The national anthem is sung at the start of each ballgame.

________________ **7.** Have the boys painted the fence yet?

________________ **8.** A great gift has been given to you.

________________ **9.** This dress has been worn only one time.

________________ **10.** What will you wear to the theater tonight?

ORAL QUIZ: Recite answers with examples.

☐ Grammar Question #81

LESSON 19: Active and Passive Voice

REVIEW RECITATION:

☐ Grammar Questions #73-81

LESSON:

Grammar Question #82: Change a sentence from active to passive voice.
Caesar conquered the Gauls. (active)
The Gauls were conquered by Caesar. (passive)

Grammar Question #83: When is the passive voice used? Give an example.
The passive voice is used when the ***doer*** *of the action is unknown, concealed, or less important than the* ***receiver*** *of the action.*

Ex. 1 The cookies were taken from the cookie jar.

Ex. 2 Rome was not built in a day.

COPYWORK:

Grammar Question #82: ____________________

Answer: ____________________

____

Grammar Question #83: ____________________

Answer: ____________________

____

Ex. 1 ____________________

Ex. 2 ____________________

PRACTICE A: All sentences are in the passive voice. Underline the verb or verb phrase in each sentence. In the blank, indicate whether the doer of the action is *known* or *unknown*. If the doer is known, it will be shown in a "by" phrase.

__________ **1.** A valuable lesson was learned that day.

__________ **2.** The trophy was stolen last night.

__________ **3.** A delicious stew was eaten by everyone.

__________ **4.** My homework paper was completely chewed up.

__________ **5.** The kittens were protected from the storm.

__________ 6. The night sky was lit up by the fireworks.

__________ 7. Soldiers in the Middle Ages were poorly paid.

__________ 8. Prayers were recited seven times a day by the monks.

PRACTICE B: Underline the verb or verb phrase in each sentence. Change the verb or verb phrase from the active voice to the passive voice, and then rewrite the sentence.

1. The parents watched their children.

____

2. Joe and Ted are building a tree house.

____

3. Many drivers break the new seatbelt law.

____

4. The referee started the game.

____

5. The mailman delivers our mail.

____

6. The strong wind blew down the old tree near our house.

____

7. Barges transport coal down the river.

____

8. Copyright law protects original work.

____

ORAL QUIZ: Recite answers with examples.

☐ Grammar Questions #82-83

UNIT III REVIEW

REVIEW RECITATION:

☐ Grammar Questions #73-83

PRACTICE A: Rewrite to find the subject, and circle it. Add "you" for an unstated subject.

1. Here is a new restaurant. ____________________

2. There are many mistakes on your math paper. ____________________

3. It is necessary to listen intently.____________________

4. Close the door. ____________________

5. Do you like pizza?____________________

PRACTICE B: Identify the kind of pronoun. Use Grammar Rules #16-18, 104-108, 128-132.

________________ **1.** *We* are going to the movie.

________________ **2.** I hid *myself* behind the curtain.

________________ **3.** *That* book is a good read.

________________ **4.** *My* book is on the table.

________________ **5.** Is *anyone* going with us?

________________ **6.** *Who* is going with us?

________________ **7.** Is John the one *who* lost his ticket?

________________ **8.** I decided, *myself,* to send the invitations.

PRACTICE C: Underline the verb or verb phrase. Ask yourself, "What or who?" before the verb to find the subject. Does the subject perform or receive the action of the verb? Tell whether the verb is in the *active* or *passive* voice.

__________________ 1. Marian is recognized by Sir Guy.

__________________ 2. Sir Guy recognizes Marian.

__________________ 3. A great archery contest was held in the forest.

__________________ 4. The Sheriff holds a great archery contest in the forest.

__________________ 5. Clorinda was recognized as an excellent archer.

__________________ 6. The Sheriff offers a large reward.

__________________ 7. A large reward is offered for the arrest of Robin Hood.

__________________ 8. Sir Guy returned to the forest with the Sheriff.

__________________ 9. Friar Tuck held them off with his quarter-staff.

__________________ 10. The Sheriff was thrown from his horse.

PRACTICE D: For each pair of sentences, decide which is *transitive* and which is *intransitive*. The transitive verb will have a direct object.

________________________ 1. He ate an apple.

________________________ 2. He eats slowly.

________________________ 3. She read aloud.

________________________ 4. She read *Adam of the Road*.

________________________ 5. He will ride his bicycle.

________________________ 6. He rides cautiously.

________________________ 7. They follow closely.

________________________ 8. They follow the path.

TEST: How many grammar questions with examples can you answer correctly?

☐ Grammar Questions #73-83

UNIT IV
Commas, Quotations, Adverbs

LESSON 20: Commas

REVIEW RECITATION: ☐ Comma Rules #1-4

LESSON:

Comma Rule #5: Use a comma to set off expressions that interrupt the sentence.

a. Nouns of direct address

Ex. Joe, will you come with us?

b. Appositives

Ex. Heidi, a young orphan, was sent to live with her grandfather.

Ex. John Mead, Ph.D., is our new teacher.

c. Parenthetical expressions

Ex. The conflict, I am sure, will be quickly resolved.

Comma Rule #6: Use a comma after words such as **Oh, Well, Yes**, and **No** when they come at the beginning of the sentence.

Ex. No, he will not be home soon. **BUT** No students were late for school.

Comma Rule #7: Use a comma before **FANBOYS (for, and, nor, but, or, yet, so)** when they join independent clauses, unless they are very short.

Ex. It snowed all morning, but the warm afternoon sun melted the snow.

COPYWORK:

Comma Rule #5: ______________________________

____

a. ______________________________

Ex. ______________________________

b. ______________________________

Ex. ______________________________

____

Ex. ______________________________

c. ______________________________

Ex. ______________________________

Comma Rule #6: ______________________________

____

Ex. ____

____

Comma Rule #7: ____

____

____

Ex. ____

____

PRACTICE A: Place a comma after each word where needed, and give the rule number.

_________ **1.** Yes I will bake a cake for the party.

_________ **2.** They are getting a ride to school but they will still be late.

_________ **3.** John your favorite dessert will be ready soon.

_________ **4.** Rex's muddy paws I believe made that trail across the kitchen floor.

_________ **5.** Joe our next door neighbor, plowed our garden.

_________ **6.** Oh taste this delicious blueberry pie!

_________ **7.** Sue baked the cake but I cleaned up the kitchen.

_________ **8.** Andy have you tried the new software?

_________ **9.** This is I am quite sure the messiest kitchen I have ever seen.

_________ **10.** Your brothers Mark and Brian are playing chess.

PRACTICE B DICTATION: Study Comma Rules #5-7 and the examples carefully. Practice writing the examples from dictation on blank paper. Check your work carefully and correct errors.

QUIZ: How many examples can you write correctly from dictation? Use blank paper.

☐ Comma Rules #5-7 Examples

LESSON 21: Quotation Marks

REVIEW RECITATION: ☐ Quotation Marks Rules #1-2

LESSON:

Quotation Marks Rule #3: In a divided quotation, each part of the quotation is enclosed in quotation marks.

Ex. 1 **"Once a king or queen in Narnia,"** said Aslan, **"always a king or queen."**

Ex. 2 **"I went into Narnia through the wardrobe,"** said Lucy. **"In Narnia I met a faun named Mr. Tumnus."**

Quotation Marks Rule #4: The second part of a divided quote **does not** begin with a capital letter unless it is a proper noun or it begins a new sentence. (Use examples above.)

Quotation Marks Rule #5: A direct quotation is set off from the rest of the sentence by **commas** or **end marks**. (Use examples above.)

Quotation Marks Rule #6: Punctuation is usually placed **inside** the quotation marks. (Use examples above.)

COPYWORK: Complete on a separate sheet of paper.

PRACTICE A: Recopy quotations, adding commas, quotation marks, and end marks where needed.

1. If you want this sword, it is yours said the priest of Nob to David for it is the only one here

___

___

2. Saul asked Why have you conspired against me with the son of Jesse

___

___

3. David accepted Abigail's gifts and said to her Go in peace to your house

___

___

4. Gird on your swords David said to his men because the battle is nigh

___

___

5. Is that your voice, my son, David Saul asked

____

____

6. David answered It is my voice, my lord, my king

____

____

7. Jonathan cried to his servant Make haste, do not delay

____

____

8. David wrote The Lord shall preserve thy going out and thy coming in from this time forth, and even for evermore

____

____

____

PRACTICE B DICTATION: Study Quotation Marks Rules #3-6 and the examples carefully. Practice writing the <u>examples</u> from dictation on blank paper. Check your work carefully and correct errors.

QUIZ: How many examples can you write correctly from dictation? Use blank paper.

☐ Quotation Marks Rules #3-6 Examples

LESSON 22: Quotation Marks

REVIEW RECITATION:

☐ Quotation Marks Rules #3-6

LESSON:

Quotation Marks Rule #7: When writing dialogue, begin a new paragraph every time the speaker changes.

> **Ex.** "Are you what they call a girl?" asked the Faun.
> "Yes, I am," answered Lucy. "What are you?" « new speaker, new paragraph indented

Quotation Marks Rule #8: Use quotation marks to enclose the titles of short works such as articles, stories, essays, chapters, poems, and songs. Italicize or underline the titles of longer works such as books, plays, long poems, paintings, sculptures, films, magazines, and newspapers.

> **Ex.** "The Lady of Shalott" BUT *The Aeneid*

Quotation Marks Rule #7: ______________________________

____

Ex. ______________________________

____

Quotation Marks Rule #8: ______________________________

____

____

____

____

Ex. ______________________________

PRACTICE A: Rewrite the following conversation between Lucy and Susan from *The Lion, the Witch and the Wardrobe*. Place quotation marks and end marks where they are needed. Remember to begin a new paragraph each time the speaker changes.

Does he know, whispered Lucy to Susan, what Aslan did for him? Does he know what the arrangement with the Witch really was? Hush! No. Of course not, said Susan. Oughtn't he to be told, said Lucy. Oh, surely not, said Susan. It would be too awful for him. Think how you'd feel if you were he. All the same I think he ought to know, said Lucy

PRACTICE B: Rewrite with either quotation marks or underlining.

1. Adam of the Road ______
2. Froggies Go to School ______
3. The Mona Lisa ______
4. The Pietá ______
5. The Sound of Music ______
6. Moby Dick ______
7. Yankee Doodle ______
8. Readers Digest ______
9. The New York Times______
10. The Emperor's New Clothes ______

PRACTICE C DICTATION: Study Quotation Marks Rules #7-8 and the examples carefully. Practice writing the examples from dictation on blank paper. Check your work carefully and correct errors.

QUIZ: How many examples can you write correctly from dictation? Use blank paper.

☐ Quotation Marks Rules #7-8 Examples

LESSON 23: Adverbs

REVIEW RECITATION:

☐ Quotation Marks Rules #1-8　　☐ Grammar Questions #22-23

LESSON:

Grammar Question #84: Give examples of nouns used as adverbs.

Ex. 1 I walked **yesterday**.

Ex. 2 I will walk **Sunday**.

Grammar Question #85: What is a common way of forming adverbs? Give an example.
(See Rules #22-23)

Many adverbs are formed by adding ***ly*** *to an adjective.*

Ex.	slow	(adjective)	He is **slow**.
	slowly	(adverb)	He walks **slowly**.

COPYWORK:

Grammar Question #84: ______________________________

Ex. 1 ______________________________

Ex. 2 ______________________________

Grammar Question #85: ______________________________

____

Answer: ______________________________

Ex. ______________________________

____

PRACTICE A: Underline the nouns which are used as adverbs in the following sentences.

1. Our visitors arrived Thursday.

2. Tomorrow the girls' softball team plays its first game.

3. His grandparents will attend the play tonight.

4. We have a recitation quiz Wednesday in our Christian Studies class.

5. I practiced reciting John 20:29 yesterday.

PRACTICE B: Change each adjective into an adverb and use it correctly in a complete sentence.

1. quick ______________________________

____

2. careful ______________________________

____

3. happy______________________________

____

4. soft ______________________________

____

5. harsh ______________________________

____

PRACTICE C: Find the *ly* word in each sentence and underline the word it modifies. Tell whether the *ly* word is an *adjective* or *adverb*.

______________ **1.** Mary is a lovely girl.

______________ **2.** The students run daily.

______________ **3.** Henry's daily schedule is grueling.

______________ **4.** The early bird gets the worm.

______________ **5.** Dairy farmers arise early every day.

______________ **6.** Sam is a friendly guy.

______________ **7.** The ugly duckling turned into a beautiful swan.

______________ **8.** He is an unlikely scholar.

ORAL QUIZ: Recite answers with examples.

☐ Grammar Questions #84-85

LESSON 24: Adverbs

REVIEW RECITATION:

☐ Grammar Questions #84-85 ☐ Quotation Marks Rules #1-8

LESSON:

***Grammar Question #86:** Adverbs of degree modify adjectives and other adverbs. Give examples.
very, so, too, really, rather, quite, especially

Ex. 1 Charlotte is **very** loyal. *very* modifies the adjective *loyal*

Ex. 2 Wilbur walks **quite** slowly. *quite* modifies the adverb *slowly*

COPYWORK:

Grammar Question #86: ____________________

____

Answer: ____________________

Ex. 1 ____________________

Ex. 2 ____________________

PRACTICE A: All of the adverbs in these sentences modify *adjectives*. Underline the adverb and circle the adjective it modifies.

1. The bitterly cold north wind brought freezing temperatures.
2. Most of the students failed the rather difficult pop quiz.
3. Unusually heavy rains flooded the fields.
4. Mrs. Watson has exceptionally bright students in her class.
5. We heard extremely loud noises in the attic.
6. Mark is a remarkably talented musician.
7. He mastered the very complicated sonata.
8. His performance at the recital was practically perfect.
9. Mark was somewhat nervous before the audition.
10. He was greatly relieved when his speech was over.

PRACTICE B: These sentences contain an adverb modifying another adverb. In #1-5, the first adverb is underlined for you. Circle the adverb it modifies. In #6-10, circle both adverbs.

1. The narrator spoke <u>so</u> quickly that I could not understand him.
2. My sister, Erin, paints <u>quite</u> well.
3. Luke <u>very</u> often finishes his homework in less than one hour.
4. We researched the topic <u>extremely</u> thoroughly.
5. Our spring vacation ended <u>too</u> soon.
6. We returned rather quickly to the school routine.
7. The baseball team will most likely have a winning season.
8. Why do the fans cheer so loudly?
9. She very carefully described the scene.
10. The choir sang remarkably well on Sunday.

DIAGRAM: Diagram the simple subject, verb, direct object, and adverbs for sentences 1-3 in Practice B.

1.

2.

3.

ORAL QUIZ: Recite answers with examples.

☐ Grammar Question #86

LESSON 25: Conjunctions

REVIEW RECITATION:

☐ Grammar Questions #84-86 ☐ Comma Rules #1-7

LESSON:

***Grammar Question #87:** What is a conjunction?
*A **conjunction** is a word that joins words, phrases, or clauses.*

***Grammar Question #88:** What are the three kinds of conjunctions?
*The three kinds of conjunctions are **coordinating**, **correlative**, and **subordinating** conjunctions.*

COPYWORK:

Grammar Question #87: ____________________

Answer: ____________________

____

Grammar Question #88: ____________________

____

Answer: ____________________

____

PRACTICE A: The conjunctions in the following sentences are circled. Underline the words joined in #1-6, and the clauses joined in #7-8.

1. Spring is a good time to begin preparing and planting a garden.
2. Select a sunny spot for vegetables and flowers.
3. Compost or manure can enrich the soil.
4. The cycle of watering, fertilizing, weeding, and mulching begins.
5. A good gardener waters and fertilizes his garden frequently.
6. The vigilant gardener must also protect his garden from insects, rabbits, and deer.
7. Some plants are easy to start from seeds, but others are better grown from seedlings.
8. You can do all these things, yet still not have a successful garden.

PRACTICE B: Add commas where needed in these sentences where the conjunctions are underlined for you. Two sentences will not need commas. Can you find them?

1. It took Marco Polo his father and his uncle three years to reach China.
2. They were welcomed by Kublai Khan in China because Marco Polo's father and uncle had been to China once before.
3. Marco's father and uncle were given important positions at the Chinese court so they remained in China for several years.
4. Marco Polo studied the Chinese language and he learned it very quickly.
5. Because he was an envoy of the Chinese monarch Marco traveled all around Asia.
6. Marco Polo his father and his uncle wanted to return to Venice but Kublai Khan did not want them to leave.
7. Finally the Chinese monarch allowed the Venetians to leave China yet it was a long time before they arrived in Venice.
8. Marco Polo was imprisoned in Genoa and he dictated the story of his many adventures in the East to a fellow prisoner.
9. His story was translated into French Italian and Latin so that many people in Europe learned about Marco Polo's adventures.
10. *The Travels of Marco Polo* may have inspired Christopher Columbus when he set out to find a trade route to the East by sailing west in 1492.

ORAL QUIZ: Recite answers with examples.

☐ Grammar Questions #87-88

LESSON 26: Conjunctions

REVIEW RECITATION:

☐ Grammar Questions #84-88

LESSON:

***Grammar Question #89:** What are coordinating conjunctions? Give examples.
The coordinating conjunctions join words, phrases, or clauses of equal importance. The coordinating conjunctions can be remembered by the acronym ***FANBOYS: for, and, nor, but, or, yet, so.***

***Grammar Question #90:** What are correlative conjunctions? Give examples.
The correlative conjunctions work in **pairs** *to join words, phrases, or clauses of equal importance.*

either … or	***neither … nor***
both … and	***not only … but (also)***
whether … or	

COPYWORK:

Grammar Question #89: ____

Answer: ____

____

____

____

Grammar Question #90: ____

____

Answer: ____

____

____

____

PRACTICE A: Underline the conjunctions in the following sentences. Indicate whether each sentence has a *coordinating conjunction* or a *correlative conjunction*.

____________________ **1.** Either Mother or Father will pick us up after swim practice.

____________________ **2.** We swim the butterfly, backstroke, breaststroke, and freestyle.

____________________ **3.** Robert will compete with both the swim team and the diving team.

____________________ **4.** She won neither the 50 meter backstroke race nor the 100 meter individual medley race.

____________________ **5.** The boys' and girls' team won the swim meet on Saturday.

____________________ **6.** Sue will be at practice on Friday, but not on Saturday.

____________________ **7.** Will you swim in the 50 meter or 100 meter backstroke race?

____________________ **8.** The coach must decide whether to have practice on Sunday or to take the day off.

____________________ **9.** Michael should win easily, for he is the best swimmer on the team.

____________________ **10.** She was tired but happy when she finished the long race.

PRACTICE B: Write your own sentences using the conjunctions as indicated.

1. Use *either … or* to join two nouns as the subject.

____

____

2. Use *and* to join two prepositional phrases.

____

____

3. Use *but* to join two seemingly contradictory adjectives.

____

____

4. Use *neither … nor* to join two verbs.

____

____

5. Use *or* to join two direct objects.

____

____

ORAL QUIZ: Recite answers with examples.

☐ Grammar Questions #89-90

UNIT IV REVIEW

REVIEW RECITATION:

- ☐ Grammar Questions #84-90
- ☐ Comma Rules #5-7
- ☐ Quotation Marks Rules #3-8

PRACTICE A: Underline the conjunctions and add commas where they are needed. Not all sentences will need commas.

1. The centurion delivered the prisoners to the captain but Paul lived in private quarters.
2. Paul was met by Christian brothers in Rome and he thanked God for them.
3. The chiefs of the Jews had neither received letters from Judea about Paul nor had they heard harmful things about him.
4. Paul spoke to the Jews in Rome about Jesus and the kingdom of God.
5. Some believed Paul's teaching but many did not believe him.
6. Paul told them that the salvation of God will be preached among the Gentiles and they will believe.
7. For two years Paul lived in Rome and taught all who came to him about Jesus Christ.
8. He also wrote letters to many churches and friends during his confinement.
9. Paul asked Timothy to bring his cloak books and parchments to Rome.
10. Paul was the great apostle to the Gentiles and he wrote many New Testament epistles.

PRACTICE B: Circle the adverbs in each sentence.

1. The rain fell steadily for seven days.
2. The fields were completely flooded.
3. Suddenly the water overflowed the banks of the river.
4. The streets of the city were totally flooded.
5. Water gradually seeped into many buildings.
6. The flood was utterly devastating to the small town.
7. Eventually the flood waters subsided.
8. Everyone worked diligently to clean up the mess.
9. The townspeople will never forget the Great Flood of 1993.
10. Those who lived through the flood vividly remember it.

PRACTICE C: Underline the adverbs in each sentence. Draw a line to the word the adverb modifies. Tell whether it modifies a verb, an adjective, or another adverb.

____________________ **1.** You seldom want to wake a sleeping baby.

____________________ **2.** Susan closed the door quietly when she entered the nursery.

____________________ **3.** The baby was sleeping very soundly in his cradle.

____________________ **4.** She tiptoed quite carefully across the wooden floor.

____________________ **5.** One of the old boards creaked noisily.

____________________ **6.** The creaking of the old floorboards almost always wakes the baby.

____________________ **7.** He was completely exhausted and did not stir at the sudden noise.

____________________ **8.** Susan deftly retrieved what she needed from the nursery.

____________________ **9.** She left the room quickly and quietly.

____________________ **10.** The baby cried loudly when he finally woke up.

PRACTICE D: Place commas where needed and give the rule number.

_________ **1.** The Butler Bears however did not win the game.

_________ **2.** Joe our star forward was injured in the game.

_________ **3.** Our guards Rodney and Rick scored more than half of the points.

_________ **4.** Dad did you buy tickets to the game?

_________ **5.** Yes it was an exciting tournament.

_________ **6.** We won the game handily but we lost our best player to injury.

_________ **7.** It was in my opinion the best game of the year.

_________ **8.** Scott have you ever seen such a high-scoring game?

_________ **9.** No I am not going out for basketball this year.

_________ **10.** We had a very good season yet we were not invited to the tournament.

PRACTICE E: Recopy, placing quotation marks, commas, and end marks where they are needed in the following sentences.

Come on Do not spare me and I'll not spare you Robin cried to George-a-Greene.
George-a-Greene responded I will not spare you, just as I did not spare your friends
Stay good George Robin exclaimed after they had fought to a draw You are the stoutest champion I have met yet I have met my match
Who are you asked George exhausted
Robin replied I am Robin Hood, and these are my two good friends
Next to King Richard, you are the man I honor the most declared George

RECITATION

Book 1 Grammar Recitation

Sentences

* 1. **What is a sentence?**
A sentence is a group of words expressing a complete thought.
Ex. Charlotte is a spider.

* 2. **What are the two parts of every sentence?**
*The two parts of every sentence are the **subject** and the **predicate**.*

* 3. **What is a subject?**
*The subject tells **who** or **what** the sentence is about.*
Ex. **Charlotte** is a spider. (*Charlotte* is the subject.)

* 4. **What is a predicate?**
*The predicate tells what the subject **is** or **does**.*
Ex. 1 Charlotte **is a spider.** (*is a spider* tells what Charlotte *is*)
Ex. 2 Charlotte **eats insects.** (*eats insects* tells what Charlotte *does*)

5. **Give the four types of sentences classified by purpose with definitions.** *The four types of sentences are declarative, imperative, interrogative, or exclamatory.*
   a. *A **declarative** sentence makes a statement.*
   b. *An **imperative** sentence gives a command or makes a request.*
   c. *An **interrogative** sentence asks a question.*
   d. *An **exclamatory** sentence expresses strong feeling.*

Parts of Speech

* 6. **Give the eight parts of speech.**
*The eight parts of speech are **noun**, **pronoun**, **adjective**, **verb**, **adverb**, **preposition**, **conjunction**, and **interjection**.*

NOUNS

* 7. **What is a noun?**
*A noun is a word that names a **person**, **place**, **thing**, or **idea**.*

8. **Name the four ways nouns may be classified.**
*Nouns may be **common** or **proper**, **concrete** or **abstract**, **collective**, and **compound**.*

9. **What is a common noun? Give examples.**
*A **common noun** names a non-specific person, place, or thing. It is **not** capitalized.*
Ex. man, country, building

10. **What is a proper noun? Give examples.**
*A **proper noun** names a specific person, place, or thing. It is capitalized.*
Ex. John, Italy, the White House

11. **What is a concrete noun? Give examples.**
*A **concrete noun** names something that can be perceived by the senses.*
Ex. table, book, desk

12. **What is an abstract noun? Give examples.**
*An **abstract noun** names a quality, characteristic, or ideal that cannot be perceived by the senses.*
Ex. truth, goodness, beauty

13. What is a compound noun? Give the three kinds with examples.
*A **compound noun** is made up of more than one word.*

a. *The words can be joined into one word.*
Ex. doorstep

b. *The words can be joined with hyphens.*
Ex. sister-in-law

c. *The words can be separate.*
Ex. United States of America

14. What is a collective noun? Give examples.
*A **collective noun** names a group.*
Ex. team, flock, class

PRONOUNS

15. Name and define the three grammar persons.
*The three grammar persons are **first person** (the person speaking), **second person** (the person spoken to), and **third person** (the person spoken about).*

*** 16. What is a pronoun?**
*A **pronoun** is a word used in place of a noun.*

17. Give the subject personal pronouns in three persons.
The subject personal pronouns are

	Singular	*Plural*
1st	***I***	***we***
2nd	***you***	***you (all)***
3rd	***he, she, it***	***they***

18. Give the object personal pronouns in three persons.
The object personal pronouns are

	Sing.	*Pl.*
1st	***me***	***us***
2nd	***you***	***you (all)***
3rd	***him, her, it***	***them***

ADJECTIVES & ADVERBS

*** 19. What is an adjective?**
*An **adjective** is a word that modifies a noun or pronoun.*

*** 20. Give the three questions adjectives answer with examples.**
*Adjectives answer the questions: **which one**, **what kind**, and **how much** or **how many**.*
Ex. 1 John gave Mary **that** rose. (which one)
Ex. 2 John gave Mary a **red** rose. (what kind)
Ex. 3 John gave Mary a **dozen** roses. (how many)

Articles, possessive nouns, and many pronouns are adjectives. They tell "which one."

*** 21. Define article and give the three English articles.**
***Articles** are words that signify nouns. **A** and **an** are the indefinite articles. **The** is the definite article. Articles are considered adjectives.*

*** 22. What is an adverb?**
*An **adverb** is a word that usually modifies a verb, but also an adjective or another adverb.*

*** 23. Give the four[1] questions adverbs answer. Give examples.**
*Adverbs answer the questions: **how** (manner), **when**, **where**, and **to what extent** (how often, how much).*
Ex. 1 He walks **gracefully**. (how)
Ex. 2 He walks **early**. (when)
Ex. 3 He walks **outside**. (where)
Ex. 4 He walks **often**. (to what extent)

VERBS

*** 24. What is a verb?**
*A **verb** is a word that shows action or being.*
Ex. Charlotte **is** a spider. (being)
Ex. Charlotte **eats** insects. (action)

*** 25. What verb shows being or existence?**
*The **to be** verb shows being or existence.*
Ex. Charlotte **is** a spider.

*** 26. Give all forms of the *to be* verb.**
*The forms of the **to be** verb are **am**, **are**, **is**, **was**, **were**, **be**, **being**, **been**.*

27. What is a physical action verb? Give examples.
*A **physical action verb** expresses action that can be perceived by the senses.*
Ex. kick, run, eat

28. What is a mental action verb? Give examples.
*A **mental action verb** expresses action that **cannot** be perceived by the senses.*
Ex. think, know, believe

1 An adverb phrase or clause may also answer **why**: *I walk **to exercise***.

*** 29. What is a verb phrase? Give examples.**
*A **verb phrase** is made up of a main verb and one or more helping verbs.*
Ex. 1 I **have been walking** for an hour.
Ex. 2 I **should have walked** yesterday.

*** 30. Give the common helping (auxiliary) verbs.**
*The **common helping verbs** are*
am, are, is, was, were, be, being, been
have, has, had
do, does, did
may, might, must
can, could
will, would
shall, should, ought

31. Give the first three English verb tenses and an example of each using *I walk*.
*The first three English verb tenses are **present**, **past**, and **future**.*
Ex. Present Tense – I **walk**
Past Tense – I **walked**
Future Tense – I **will walk**

Book 2 Grammar Recitation

Sentences

32. What is the best way to find the subject of a sentence?
*Locate the verb, and then ask the question **who** or **what** before the verb.*

33. Give an example of a word that can be used as more than one part of speech.
***Total** can be used as a noun, verb, or adjective.*
Ex. 1 The **total** is one hundred. (noun)
Ex. 2 I will **total** the score. (verb)
Ex. 3 It was a **total** disaster. (adjective)

34. What is the difference between the simple subject and the complete subject? Give examples.
a. *The simple subject is the principal word the sentence is about.*
Ex. The best **class** in school is grammar.
Simple subject: *class*
b. *The complete subject is the simple subject with all its modifiers.*
Ex. The best class in school is grammar.
Complete subject: *The best class in school*

35. What is the difference between the simple predicate and the complete predicate?
a. *The simple predicate is the verb, including helping verbs.*
Ex. John **is learning** Latin in school.
Simple predicate: *is learning*
b. *The complete predicate is the verb with all its modifiers.*
Ex. John **is learning Latin in school**.
Complete predicate: *is learning Latin in school*

36. Give an example of a compound subject and a compound verb.
Ex. 1 Compound Subject:
Fern and **Avery** went to bed early the night before the County Fair.
Ex. 2 Compound Verb:
Wilbur **stared** back at the crowd and **tried** to look his best.

Verbs

37. What are the principal parts of a verb?
The principal parts are the four basic forms of the verb.

* **38. Give the names of the four[1] principal parts of an English verb with examples using the verb *walk*.**

the infinitive	*to walk*
the present participle	*walking*
the past tense	*walked*
the past participle	*have walked (has walked)*

* **39. What is the infinitive? Give examples.**
*The **infinitive** is the dictionary form of the verb preceded by the word **to**. The infinitive usually functions as a noun.*
Ex. Mary wants **to learn** Latin.
To learn is a noun, the direct object of the verb *wants*.
Ex. To be or not **to be**, that is the question. **To die, to sleep, to dream** (from *Hamlet*).
The *to* of the infinitive is not a preposition. It is called a *particle*. The infinitive is so called because it is the pure form of the verb, not finite, or limited by number and person.

1 The present participle is technically not a principal part since it can always be derived from the infinitive by adding **ing**.

*** 40. What is a participle? What are the two forms? Give examples.** *(The participle is half verb and half adjective.)*

*A **participle**[2] is an adjective formed from a verb (a verbal adjective). The two participles are the **present participle** and the **past participle**.*

Ex. 1 Present Participle:
The **conquering** Gauls stormed the gates of Rome.

Ex. 2 Past Participle:
The **conquered** Gauls surrendered to Caesar.

*** 41. How is the present participle formed?**
*The present participle is formed by adding **ing** to the dictionary form.*

*** 42. How is the past participle formed?**
*The regular past participle is formed by adding **d** or **ed** to the dictionary form.*

*** 43. What is a regular verb?**
*A **regular verb** is one that forms its past and past participle by adding **d** or **ed** to the dictionary form.*
Ex. I walk, I walked, I have walked

*** 44. What is an irregular verb?**
*An **irregular verb** is one that does not form its past and past participle by adding **d** or **ed** to the dictionary form.*
Ex. I see, I saw, I have seen

2 In a regular verb the past tense and past participle have the same form. (#38, 45) Participles are also used with helping verbs to form verb phrases. (#29, 30)

Book 2 Grammar Recitation

45. Give the principal parts of the regular verbs *live, play, look,* and *learn.*

to live	*living*	*lived*	*have lived*
to play	*playing*	*played*	*have played*
to look	*looking*	*looked*	*have looked*
to learn	*learning*	*learned*	*have learned*

46. Give the principal parts of the irregular verbs *see, write, come, do, fly,* and *go.*

to see	*seeing*	*saw*	*have seen*
to write	*writing*	*wrote*	*have written*
to come	*coming*	*came*	*have come*
to do	*doing*	*did*	*have done*
to fly	*flying*	*flew*	*have flown*
to go	*going*	*went*	*have gone*

*** 47. What are the names of the six English tenses?**
Present
Past
Future
Present Perfect[3]
Past Perfect
Future Perfect

48. Give the first person singular of the six English verb tenses using the verb *walk.*[4]

Present	*I walk (he, she, it walks)*
Past	*I walked*
Future	*I will walk*
Present Perfect	*I have walked (he **has** walked)*
Past Perfect	*I had walked*
Future Perfect	*I will have walked*

3 Some grammars omit the word *present* for this tense.
As in Latin, the word *perfect* means completed. The present perfect tense describes an action started in the past and completed in the present or with a continuing effect into the present.
4 For non-Latin students, conjugate the present and present perfect in all three persons, singular and plural.

I walk	we walk	I have walked	we have walked
you walk	you all walk	you have walked	you all have walked
he, she, it walks	they walk	he, she, it has walked	they have walked

* 49. **What are the two main aspects of English verbs?**
*English verbs have **progressive** and **emphatic** forms.*

50. **What is the progressive verb form?**
*The **progressive verb** form shows continuous action and consists of the present participle with forms of the **to be** verb as helping verbs.*

51. **Give the progressive forms for the first person singular of the six English verb tenses using the verb *walk*.**[5]

Present	*I am walking*
Past	*I was walking*
Future	*I will be walking*
Present Perfect	*I have been walking*
Past Perfect	*I had been walking*
Future Perfect	*I will have been walking*

52. **What is the emphatic form? Give examples.**
*The **emphatic form** shows emphasis or unusual stress. It is found in only two tenses, the present and past. It uses the helping verbs **do**, **does**, or **did**.*
Ex. 1 Present Emphatic – **I do walk** **(he, she, it does)**
Ex. 2 Past Emphatic – **I did walk**

53. **What are the two ways the words of a verb phrase can be separated? Give examples.** (See #29)

a. *The subject is placed between the helping verb and the main verb in questions.*
Ex. **Is** Wilbur **walking**? **Does** Wilbur **walk**?

b. *An adverb can be placed between the helping verb and the main verb.*
Ex. Wilbur **is *not* walking**. Wilbur **is *always* walking**. (*Not* and *always* are adverbs.)

[5] Make sure students can conjugate present, past, and present perfect in full. (See #48 footnote for pattern.)

54. **Give eight words that are always adverbs and often interrupt a verb phrase.**
Ever, never, not, almost, always, hardly, scarcely, seldom

Questions

55. **What are the two types of direct questions?**
The two types of direct questions are questions introduced by question words and yes/no questions.

56. **How do you form a yes or no question? Give an example.**
To form a yes/no question, put a helping verb first.
Ex. He likes Latin. (statement)
Does he like Latin? **Is** he liking Latin? **Did** he like Latin? (questions)

* 57. **What are the six common question words?**
*The six common question words are **who***, **what**, **when**, **where**, **why**, **how**.* **whose, whom, which*

Book 3 Grammar Recitation

Sentence Complements

* **58. What is a sentence complement? Give the four complements.**[6]
*A **complement** is one or more words in the predicate that complete the meaning of the subject and verb. The four complements are **predicate nominative**, **predicate adjective**, **direct object**, and **indirect object**.*

59. What parts of speech are NOT complements? (See #84-86)
Adverbs and prepositional phrases are not complements.
Ex. 1 Wilbur walks **in the barn**. (*In the barn* is p.p. telling *where*.)
Ex. 2 Wilbur walks **slowly**. (*Slowly* is an adverb telling *how*.)

* **60. Define predicate nominative. Give an example.**
*A **predicate nominative** is a noun or pronoun that follows a **linking verb** and renames the subject.*
Ex. Wilbur is a **pig**.
The predicate nominative answers the question *what* or *who* after a linking verb.

* **61. Define predicate adjective. Give an example.**
*A **predicate adjective** is an adjective that follows a **linking verb** and modifies the subject.*
Ex. Wilbur is **tired**.
The predicate adjective answers the question *what* after a linking verb.

* **62. What question does the predicate nominative or predicate adjective answer?**
*The predicate nominative or adjective answers the question **what** or **who** after a **linking** verb.*

* **63. What is a linking verb?** (See #25-26)
*A **linking verb** connects the subject with a noun or adjective in the predicate. It shows **being**, not action.*

* **64. What is the most common linking verb?**
*The **to be** verb is the most common linking verb.*

65. Forms of the *to be* verb may be used as linking verbs or helping verbs. Give an example of each.
Ex. 1 Wilbur **is** a pig. (linking verb)
Ex. 2 Wilbur **is walking** to the barn.
(helping verb for main verb, *walking*)

66. What verbs in addition to the *to be* verb can be linking verbs?
appear, become, feel, grow, look, remain, seem, smell, sound, stay, taste

67. Use *smell* as an action verb and a linking verb.
*Jane **smells** the rose.* (action verb)
*The rose **smells** wonderful.* (linking verb)
*Substitute *"is"* (*am/are*) for the verb to determine if it is an action or a linking verb. Your substitution will only make sense when it is a linking verb. (*The rose is wonderful* makes sense. *Jane is the rose* does not make sense.)

* **68. Define direct object. Give an example.**
*A **direct object** is a noun or pronoun that receives the action of the verb.*
Ex. The magister teaches **Latin**.

6 The objective complement is not covered in this course.

*** 69. What question does a direct object answer?**
*The direct object answers the question **what** or **whom** after an **action** verb.*

70. What is a complementary infinitive? Give an example.
A complementary infinitive is an infinitive used as a direct object.
Ex. Wilbur loves **to learn**. Wilbur wants **to eat**.

*** 71. What is an indirect object? Give an example.**[7]
*The **indirect object** precedes the direct object and tells to whom or for whom the action of the verb is done.*
Ex. 1 The magister teaches **me** Latin.
Ex. 2 The magister gives **John** a test.

72. What kind of verbs usually have indirect objects?
Giving and telling verbs usually have indirect objects.

7 Rewriting each sentence with the indirect object as the object of the preposition **to** does not change the meaning. (The magister teaches Latin to **me**. The magister gives a test to **John**.) Although an English grammar would refer to **me** and **John** as prepositional objects, grammatically they are still indirect objects.

Book 3 Grammar Recitation

Finding the Subject

73. Give five difficulties in finding the subject, with examples.

a. *In sentences expressing a command or request, the subject is always **you**.*
Ex. Study your Latin.
(You) Study your Latin.

b. *To find a subject in a question, turn the question into a statement.*
Ex. What lesson did you study? (question)
You did study what lesson. (statement)
Subject: *You;* Verb: *did study*

c. *The subject of a sentence is never a prepositional phrase.*
Ex. **Neither** of the students **studied** his Latin.
The subject and verb is *neither studied*. *Students* is the object of the preposition *of*.

d. ***Here** is not usually the subject of a verb.*
Ex. Here is the book.
The **book** is here. (reworded)
Here is an adverb telling where. *Book* is the subject of the verb *is*.

e. *The expletives* **there** and **it** are not usually subjects of a verb.*
Ex. 1 **There** are books on both tables.
Books are on both tables. (reworded)
Books is the subject of the verb *are*. *There* gets the sentence started.
Ex. 2 **It** is important to study Latin.
To study Latin is important. (reworded)
To study is the subject of the verb *is*. *It* gets the sentence started.

*An **expletive** is a word with no grammatical function.

Pronouns

* 74. **Give the eight kinds of pronouns in pairs.** (See #16-18)
Personal and Possessive
Intensive and Reflexive
Relative and Interrogative
Demonstrative and Indefinite

75. **Many pronouns can also function as what part of speech?**
Many pronouns also function as adjectives.

76. **Give the pronoun forms of the possessive pronoun.**
mine, yours, his, hers, its, ours, yours, theirs

77. **Give the adjective forms of the possessive pronoun.**
my, your, his, her, its, our, your, their

Verbs

* 78. **What is a transitive verb? Give examples.**
A ***transitive*** *verb requires a direct object to complete its meaning.*
Ex. 1 John ignored the insult.
Ex. 2 John completed his lesson.

* 79. **What is an intransitive verb? Give examples.**
An ***intransitive*** *verb does not require a direct object to complete its meaning.*
Ex. **Sleep, laugh, look, die,** and the **to be** verb are always intransitive.

80. **Many verbs can be used both transitively and intransitively. Give examples.**
Ex. 1 I eat pizza. (transitive, *pizza* is a direct object)
Ex. 2 I eat every day. (intransitive, *every day* is an adverb)

* 81. **What is the difference between the active and passive voice?**
In the ***active*** *voice, the subject performs the action of the verb. In the* ***passive*** *voice, the subject receives the action of the verb.*

82. **Change a sentence from active to passive voice.**
Caesar conquered the Gauls. (active)
The Gauls were conquered by Caesar. (passive)

83. **When is the passive voice used? Give an example.**
The passive voice is used when the ***doer*** *of the action is unknown, concealed, or less important than the* ***receiver*** *of the action.*
Ex. The cookies were taken from the cookie jar.
Ex. Rome was not built in a day.

Adverbs
Modifying Verbs

84. **Give examples of nouns used as adverbs.**
Ex. 1 I walked **yesterday**.
Ex. 2 I will walk **Sunday**.

85. **What is a common way of forming adverbs? Give an example.** (See #22-23)
Many adverbs are formed by adding ***ly*** *to an adjective.*
Ex. slow (adjective) He is **slow**.
slowly (adverb) He walks **slowly**.

Adverbs

Modifying Adjectives and Other Adverbs

* **86. Adverbs of degree modify adjectives and other adverbs. Give examples.**
very, so, too, really, rather, quite, especially
Ex. 1 Charlotte is **very** loyal. (*very* modifies the adjective *loyal*)
Ex. 2 Wilbur walks **quite** slowly. (*quite* modifies the adverb *slowly*)

Conjunctions

* **87. What is a conjunction?**
A ***conjunction*** *is a word that joins words, phrases, or clauses.*

* **88. What are the three kinds of conjunctions?**
The three kinds of conjunctions are ***coordinating, correlative,*** *and* ***subordinating*** *conjunctions.*

* **89. What are coordinating conjunctions? Give examples.**
The coordinating conjunctions join words, phrases, or clauses of equal importance. The coordinating conjunctions can be remembered by the acronym **FANBOYS**: ***for, and, nor, but, or, yet, so.***

* **90. What are correlative conjunctions? Give examples.**
The correlative conjunctions work in ***pairs*** *to join words, phrases, or clauses of equal importance.*

either … or	***neither … nor***
both … and	***not only … but (also)***
whether … or	

Nouns and Pronouns

* **104. What are the reflexive and intensive pronouns?**
(See #16-18, 74)
The reflexive and intensive pronouns are the self-pronouns: ***myself, yourself, himself, herself, itself, oneself, ourselves, yourselves, themselves***

* **105. What is a reflexive pronoun? Give examples.**
The ***reflexive pronoun*** *is always an object—direct, indirect, or prepositional—and refers back to the subject of the verb.*
Ex. 1 Mary hurt **herself**. (direct object)
Ex. 2 Mary told **herself** a story. (indirect object)
Ex. 3 Mary wrote a note to **herself**. (the object of preposition *to*)

* **106. What is an intensive pronoun? Give examples.**
The ***intensive pronoun*** *is used to show emphasis.*
Ex. 1 Caesar **himself** led the charge.
Ex. 2 We met Caesar **himself** in the forum.

* **107. What are the demonstrative pronouns?**
The demonstrative pronouns point out a person or thing. The pronouns ***this*** *and* ***these*** *point to something near, and the pronouns* ***that*** *and* ***those*** *point to something far.*

108. Give an example of a demonstrative pronoun used as a pronoun and as an adjective.
Ex. Mary likes **that**. (pronoun)
Mary likes **that** book. (adjective)

Pronouns

*** 128. What is a relative pronoun?** (See #74)
*A **relative pronoun** begins a subordinate adjective clause and refers to a stated or understood antecedent.*

*** 129. What is an antecedent?**
*An **antecedent** is the noun or pronoun in the main clause that the relative pronoun, adjective, or adverb refers back to.*

*** 130. Give the relative pronouns.**
*The **relative pronouns** are **who, whose, whom, which, that**.*

*** 131. Define and give the interrogative pronouns.**
*The **interrogative pronouns** ask questions. They are **who, whose, whom, which, what**.*

*** 132. Define and give ten indefinite pronouns.**
*The **indefinite pronouns** often refer to unnamed, non-specific antecedents. Ten indefinite pronouns are **all, any, each, few, many, other, some, several, somebody, whoever**.*

Capitalization & Punctuation Style Sheets

CAPITALIZATION RULES

Capitalization Rules	Examples
Capitalization Rule #1: Capitalize the first word of a sentence, the pronoun **I**, and the interjection **O**.	**B**less us, **O** God. **W**oe is me, **O** Hector! **H**enry and **I** walked to school.
Capitalization Rule #2: Capitalize all words that refer to God, but not pagan gods.	In **G**od we trust. In the year of the **L**ord. The Greek god Poseidon is lord of the sea.
Capitalization Rule #3: Capitalize words that show family relationship if used as a name, but not if preceded by a possessive pronoun.	I asked **M**om and **A**unt **M**ary to teach me to cook. I asked my mom and my aunt to teach me to cook.
Capitalization Rule #4: Capitalize the first word and all important words in titles of books, poems, stories, films, works of art, and magazines.	We memorize the poem "**H**oratius at the **B**ridge." (names of short works are enclosed in quotation marks) We watched the movie *Anne of Green Gables*. The ***P**ieta* is a sculpture by Michelangelo. (names of works of art, movies, and books are also italicized)
Capitalization Rule #5: Capitalize months of the year, days of the week, A.M.* and P.M.*, B.C. and A.D. Do not capitalize seasons unless part of a title. *A.M. and P.M. are now acceptable as uppercase or lowercase, but we will capitalize them in our grammar books.	I was born on **T**uesday, **F**ebruary 21, at 3:00 **P.M.*** Julius Caesar was assassinated in 44 **B.C.** We have a hayride in the fall. The **F**all **F**estival was a success.
Capitalization Rule #6: Capitalize compass directions when referring to regions of the country or world, but not when used as directions.	He lived in the **F**ar **E**ast for many years. The **S**outh has produced many great writers. We study **S**outhern writers. He was driving south on I-65.
Capitalization Rule #7: Capitalize titles of persons when they precede a name or when used in place of a name: Dr., Mr., Mrs., Senator, President, Captain, etc.	I see **D**r. Watson and **M**r. and **M**rs. Smith. Hello, **C**aptain! **BUT** Is there a captain on the ship? The **P**resident was shot in Ford's Theater. **BUT** John is the president of our club.
Capitalization Rule #8: Capitalize the salutation and closing of a letter.	**D**ear Sally, **S**incerely, **Y**ours truly,
Capitalization Rule #9: Capitalize the first word of a direct quote.	Charlotte said, "**Y**ou're terrific."
Capitalization Rule #10: Capitalize proper nouns and adjectives.	**Q**ueen **V**ictoria, **M**rs. **A**rable, **M**ary, **V**ictorian literature
a. Capitalize names of persons.	**Q**ueen **V**ictoria, **M**rs. **A**rable, **M**ary (noun) **V**ictorian literature (adjective)
b. Capitalize geographical names: mountains, rivers, cities, states, streets, and parks.	**L**ondon, **E**ngland **L**ouisville, **K**entucky **P**acific **O**cean **R**ocky **M**ountains **B**irchwood **A**venue **Y**ellowstone **N**ational **P**ark
c. Capitalize historical periods and events.	the **M**iddle **A**ges the **R**enaissance **R**econstruction the **W**orld **C**up
d. Capitalize names of holidays.	the **F**ourth of **J**uly **T**hanksgiving **D**ay **M**emorial **D**ay
e. Capitalize names of religions.	**I**slam, **H**induism, **J**udaism, **C**hristianity

Capitalization Rules	Examples
f. Capitalize names of organizations.	**R**ed **C**ross, **F**irst **N**ational **B**ank
g. Capitalize brand names.	**N**ike shoes, **F**ord cars
h. Capitalize names of nations, nationalities, ethnic groups, languages.	**I**taly, **I**talian food **H**ispanic **J**ewish
i. Capitalize names of planets and stars; moon and sun are not capitalized.	**M**ars, **S**irius, **B**etelgeuse, **E**arth (when referring to the planet and not the ground) moon, sun
j. Capitalize names of buildings, monuments, ships.	the **W**hite **H**ouse, the **A**lamo (buildings/monuments) *Monitor, Merrimac* (names of ships are also italicized)
k. Capitalize specific courses.	Chemistry 101 **BUT** I like chemistry.

PUNCTUATION RULES

End Marks Rules	Examples
End Marks Rule #1: Use a period at the end of a statement.	Punctuation is interesting.
End Marks Rule #2: Use a period at the end of an abbreviation.	**St., Rd., Ln., Ave., Mr., Mrs., Dr., Sr., Jr., Capt., etc., B.C.**
a. Do not use a period for abbreviations of well-known phrases or names of organizations.	**KJV** (King James Version) **CA** **KY** (states) **UN** (United Nations) **USPS** (United States Postal Service)
b. Use a period after each initial that is part of a name.	**C. S. Lewis** (Clive Staples Lewis) **J. R. R. Tolkien** (John Ronald Reuel Tolkien)
End Marks Rule #3: Use an exclamation mark at the end of an exclamation.	What a beautiful sunrise!
End Marks Rule #4: Use a question mark at the end of a question.	What time is it?
End Marks Rule #5: An imperative sentence may be followed by a period or an exclamation mark, depending upon the force intended.	Please close the door. Come here right now!

PUNCTUATION RULES

Comma Rules See also Quotation Marks Rules #5, 6	**Examples**
Comma Rule #1: Use a comma to separate items in a series.	I have **pens**, **pencils**, **paper**, and **books** in my backpack.
Comma Rule #2: Use a comma to separate two or more adjectives of equal value preceding a noun.	It was a gray, dreary morning. **BUT*** Our large black cat is lazy. *The order of *gray* and *dreary* can be reversed but not *large* and *black*.
Comma Rule #3: Use a comma to separate items in addresses and dates.	Albany, New York March 7, 1990
Comma Rule #4: Use a comma after the salutation of a friendly letter and the closing of any letter.	Dear Sue, Sincerely, Yours truly,
Comma Rule #5: Use a comma to set off expressions that interrupt the sentence.	
a. Nouns of direct address	Joe, will you come with us?
b. Appositives	Heidi, a young orphan, was sent to live with her grandfather. *Titles and academic degrees are set off like appositives.* John Mead, Ph.D., is our new teacher. Louis Carroll, M.D., moved in next door.
c. Parenthetical expressions	The conflict, I am sure, will be quickly resolved.
Comma Rule #6: Use a comma after words such as **Oh**, **Well**, **Yes**, and **No** when they come at the beginning of the sentence and do not modify another word.	No, he will not be home soon. **BUT** No students were late for school.
Comma Rule #7: Use a comma before **FANBOYS (for, and, nor, but, or, yet, so)** when they join independent clauses, unless the clauses are very short.	It snowed all morning, but the warm afternoon sun melted the snow.

Apostrophe Rules	**Examples**
Apostrophe Rule #1: Add an apostrophe to form the possessive of a noun ending in **s**.	All the boys' shoes were wet and muddy. Chris' shoes are new. or Chris's shoes are new.
Apostrophe Rule #2: Add an apostrophe **s** ('s) to form the possessive of a noun **not** ending in **s**.	The bird's wing is broken.
Apostrophe Rule #3: Add an apostrophe to indicate where letters have been omitted in a contraction.	He'll be home soon.

Quotation Mark Rules	Examples
Quotation Marks Rule #1: Use quotation marks to enclose a direct quotation—a person's exact words. Do not use quotation marks with indirect quotations.	Aslan said, **"Once a king or queen in Narnia, always a king or queen."** Aslan said that you will always be a king in Narnia. (no marks)
Quotation Marks Rule #2: A direct quotation begins with a capital letter.	(Note example above.)
Quotation Marks Rule #3: In a divided quotation, each part of the quotation is enclosed in quotation marks.	**"Once a king or queen in Narnia,"** said Aslan, **"always a king or queen."** **"I went into Narnia through the wardrobe,"** said Lucy. **"In Narnia I met a faun named Mr. Tumnus."**
Quotation Marks Rule #4: The second part of a divided quote **does not** begin with a capital letter unless it is a proper noun or it begins a new sentence.	(Note examples above.)
Quotation Marks Rule #5: A direct quotation is set off from the rest of the sentence by **commas** or **end marks**.	"Once a king or queen in Narnia**,**" said Aslan**,** "always a king or queen." "Are you what they call a girl**?**" asked the Faun.
Quotation Marks Rule #6: Punctuation is usually placed **inside** the quotation marks.	(Note examples above.)
Quotation Marks Rule #7: When writing dialogue, begin a new paragraph every time the speaker changes.	"Are you what they call a girl?" asked the Faun. "Yes, I am," answered Lucy. "What are you?" « new speaker, new paragraph
Quotation Marks Rule #8: Use quotation marks to enclose the titles of short works such as articles, stories, essays, chapters, poems, and songs. Italicize or underline the titles of longer works such as books, plays, long poems, paintings, sculptures, films, magazines, and newspapers.	"The Lady of Shalott" BUT the *Aeneid*

Colon & Hyphen Rules	Examples
Colon Rule #1: Use a colon between the hour and the minute.	We will begin at **4:00** P.M.
Colon Rule #2: Use a colon between chapter and verse for references to religious holy texts like the Bible, the Quran, the Torah, etc.	John 3:16
Hyphen Rule #1: Hyphens are used in writing compound number words from twenty-one through ninety-nine.	My grandfather will be **ninety-five** this year.
Hyphen Rule #2: Hyphens are used in many compound words.	My **great-grandmother** is a **first-class** cook.

DIAGRAMMING

DIAGRAMMING

Diagramming gives students a picture of sentence structure, and is an effective technique to help students understand grammar. The diagram begins with a horizontal line that contains the backbone of the sentence—the subject and the verb. Crossing over this line is a vertical line that divides the sentence into its two parts, the simple subject on the left and the verb on the right. Adjectives and adverbs are written on slanted lines below the words they modify. The subject and all of its modifiers is called the complete subject. The verb and all of its modifiers is called the complete predicate.

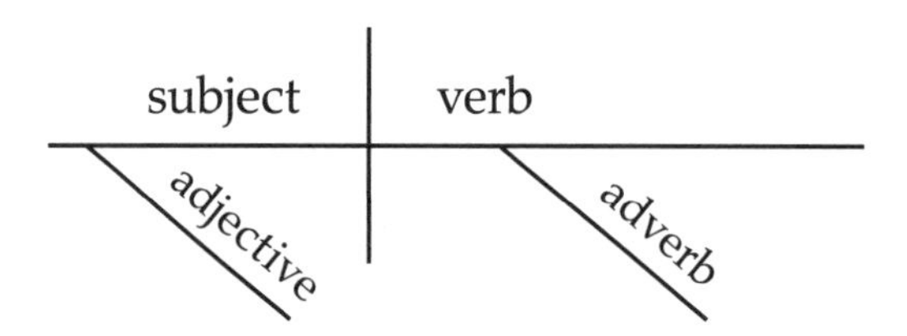

Complements are written on the horizontal line and separated from the verb by a line which does not cross over the base line. If the complement is a direct object, the vertical line is perpendicular to the base line.

subject | verb | direct object

If the complement is a predicate nominative or adjective, the vertical line is slanted to the left.

subject | verb \ pred. nom.

subject | verb \ pred. adj.

Adjectives are written on slanted lines below the subject or predicate nominative (or other nouns and pronouns in more complex sentences). Adverbs are written on slanted lines below the verb or other adverbs and adjectives.

Possessive nouns, possesive pronouns, and articles are considered adjectives.

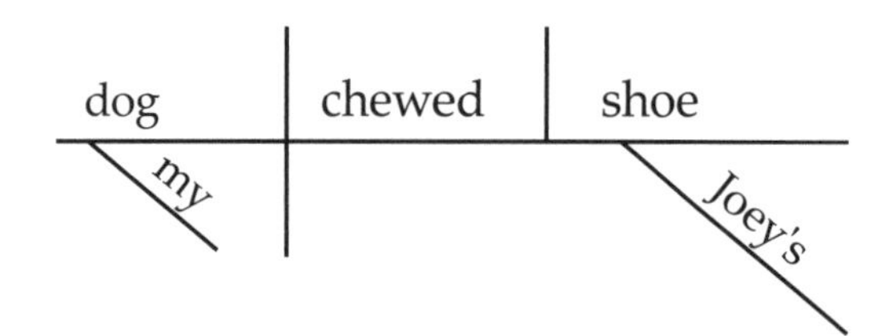

Diagramming Compound Subjects

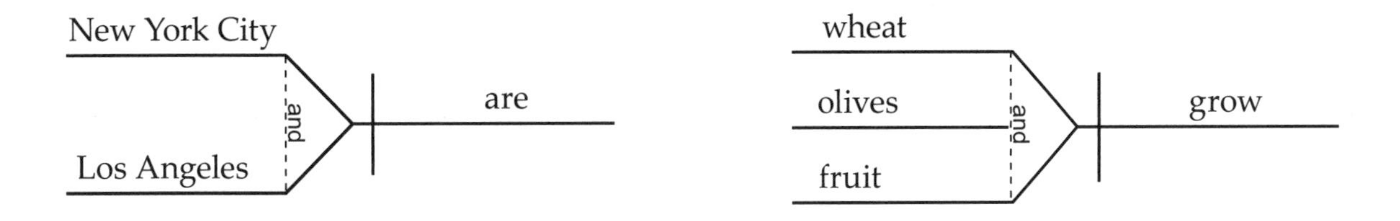

Diagramming Compound Verbs

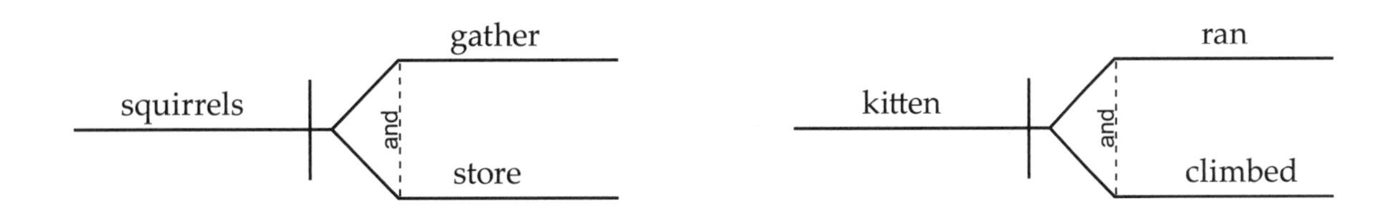

Diagramming Compound Direct Objects

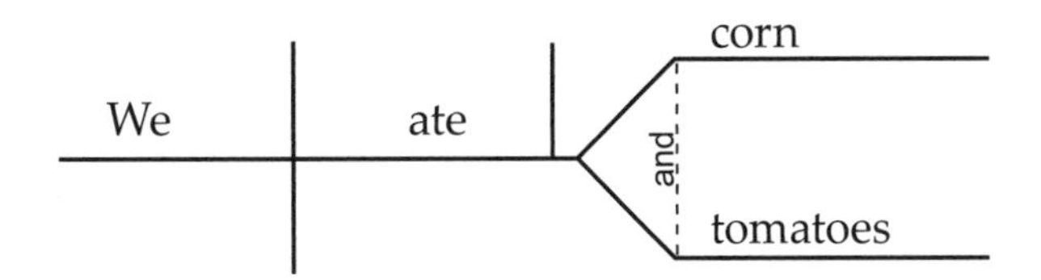

One way to help students understand grammar is to label each word in a sentence. Here is a list of sentence parts and their abbreviations. Students can write these abbreviations above each word and then diagram each sentence. Here are the labels that will be used in this text.

SN	Subject noun
V	Verb
Adv	Adverb
SP	Subject pronoun
V-t	Verb-transitive
DO	Direct object
CI	Complementary infinitive
PA	Predicate adjective
LV	Linking verb
PrN	Predicate nominative
A	Article
IO	Indirect object
P	Preposition
OP	Object of preposition
G	Gerund
Pa	Participle
Inf	Infinitive
( )	Encloses a subordinate clause

SENTENCE PATTERN #1
Subject + Verb

If an action verb is intransitive, all that is needed for a sentence is the backbone—a subject and a verb. The subject can be a noun or a pronoun, and other modifiers such as adverbs and adjectives do not change the basic pattern.

The verb can be one word or it can be a verb phrase. A verb phrase contains a main verb plus all of its helping verbs.

SN V Adv.
Mary is walking today.

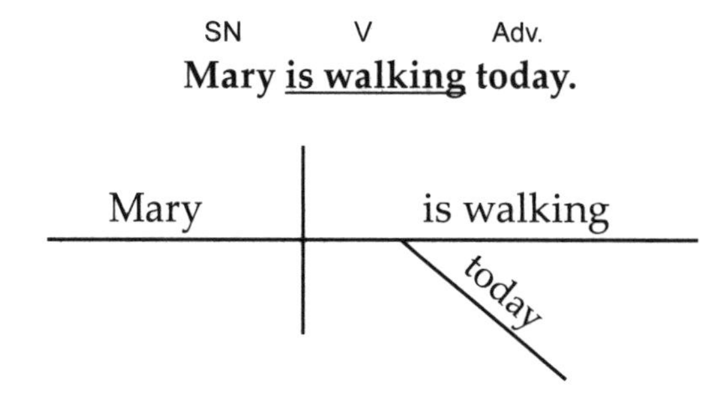

SENTENCE PATTERNS #2 THROUGH #5

Sentence Pattern #1 above is the only one of the five basic sentence patterns that does not have **complements**. Most verbs need a completer to *complete* their meaning. If I say *Mary likes*, you do not feel like I have finished my thought. You want to know *what* or *whom* Mary likes. All of the four remaining sentence patterns have complements. The four complements are *direct object, predicate nominative, predicate adjective,* and *indirect object.*

SENTENCE PATTERN #2
Subject + Verb + Direct Object

The first type of complement is the direct object. Typical English word order is *subject-verb-direct object.* The direct object can be a noun or pronoun. To find the direct object, ask "What or whom?" after the subject and verb. A verb that is completed by a direct object is called a transitive verb. The action is carried over to another noun or pronoun in the predicate.

SN V-t DO
Mary likes the queen.

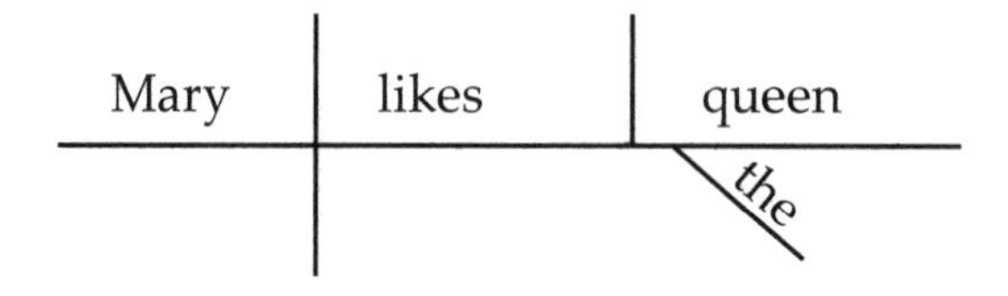

The direct object can also be a more complex construction, such as the *Complementary Infinitive (CI).*

SN V-t CI
Mary likes to swim.

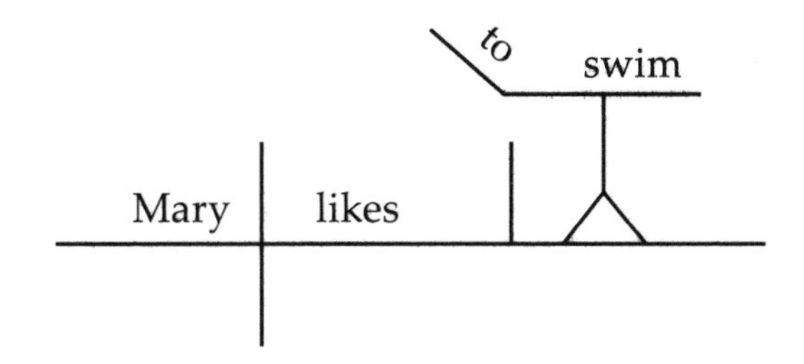

SENTENCE PATTERN #3
Subject + Verb + Predicate Adjective

Verbs that are completed by a predicate nominative or adjective are called *linking verbs.* They are *intransitive* because they are not completed by a direct object. If an adjective follows the linking verb and describes the subject, it is called a *predicate adjective* and is in the predicate part of the sentence.

SN LV PA
Mary is good.

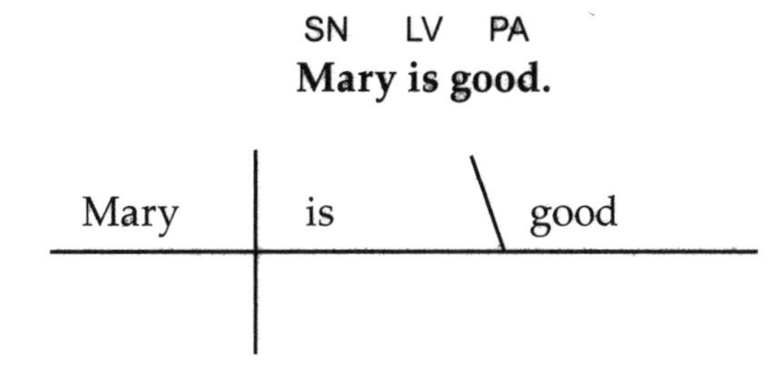

SENTENCE PATTERN #4
Subject + Verb + Predicate Nominative

If a noun (or pronoun) follows the linking verb and renames the subject, it is called a *predicate nominative.* It renames the subject, but it is in the predicate part of the sentence.

SN LV PrN
Mary is a girl.

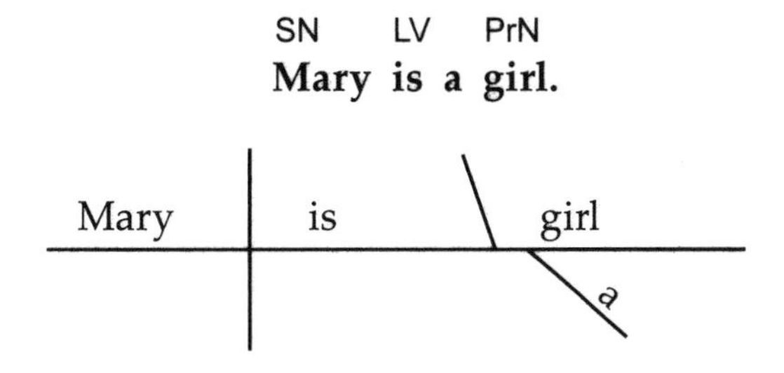

Again, modifiers do not change the basic sentence pattern.

SN LV Adj. PrN Adv.
Mary is a good girl today.

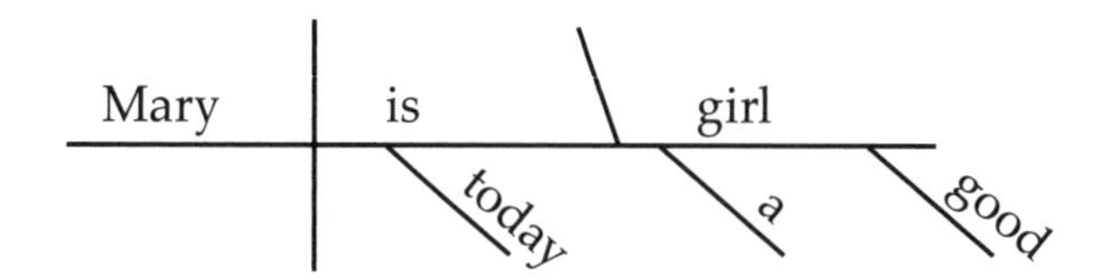

SENTENCE PATTERN #5
Subject + Verb + Indirect Object + Direct Object

Sentences that have direct objects may also have an indirect object. Verbs that typically have indirect objects are giving and telling verbs. The indirect object usually precedes the direct object. To diagram an indirect object, draw a slanted line under the verb and write the indirect object on a connecting horizontal line.

SN V-t IO DO
Mary gave Mark a gift.

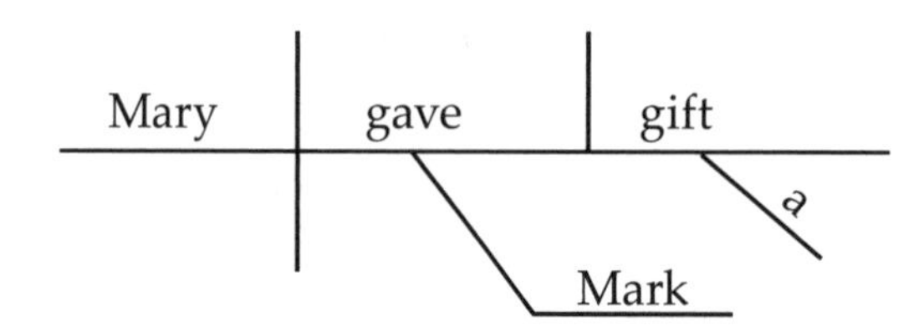

English often uses a prepositional phrase for the indirect object. Grammatically the prepositional phrase functions as an indirect object even though it is not so designated. The sentence below means exactly the same thing as the one above.

SN V-t A DO P OP
Mary gave a gift to Mark.

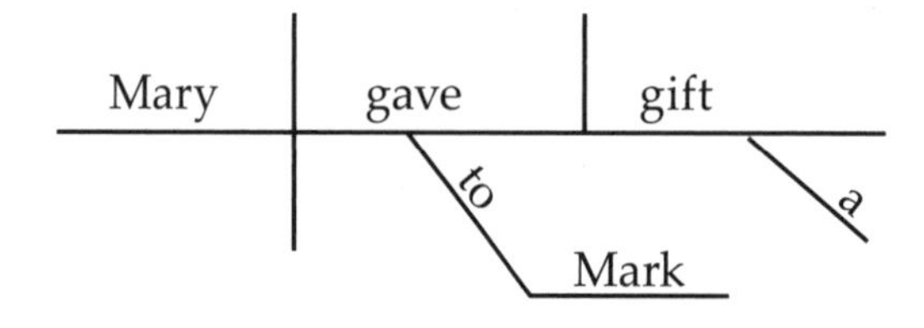

MISCELLANEOUS
Adverbs of Degree

Adverbs usually modify verbs and are diagrammed as shown on the facing page. Less often adverbs modify adjectives or other adverbs. Adverbs of degree, such as *very, too, really,* etc., are diagrammed as shown below.

SN V Adv. Adv.
Mary spoke very quickly.

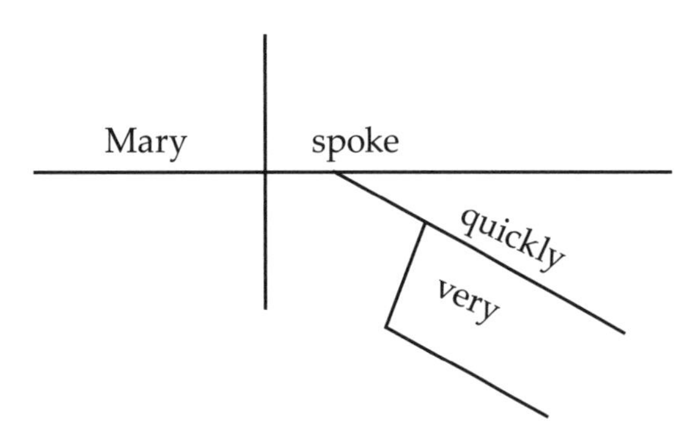